Preschool Sensory Scan for Educators

(Preschool SENSE)

A Collaborative Tool for Occupational Therapists
and Early Childhood Teachers

by Carol S. Kranowitz, M.A.

Author of *The Out-of-Sync Child*,
The Out-of-Sync Child Has Fun, and
The Goodenoughs Get in Sync

Sensory
RESOURCES LLC
Las Vegas

This program is intended for use under the direction of a qualified occupational therapist or other professional.

All trademarks are the property of their respective owners.

Cover by Lauren Motley/RedHare Studio

Author photo © Beverly Rezneck

First Edition, January 2006

Published by

2500 Chandler Avenue, Suite 3
Las Vegas, NV 89120-4064
Tel. 888-357-5867
Fax 702-891-8899
Email: Info@SensoryResources.com
www.SensoryResources.com

Ordering Information for Forms

All of the forms in this book are available separately in *Forms Packet for Preschool SENSE* (ISBN-13: 978-1-931615-24-2 or ISBN-10: 1-913615-24-1) available from Sensory Resources' website at www.SensoryResources.com or wherever fine books are sold. Each *Forms Packet for Preschool SENSE* includes sufficient forms for eight children. Use additional copies of the *Forms Packet* for larger groups of children.

CIP data is available from the publisher or the Library of Congress.

ISBN-13: 978-1-931615-18-1
ISBN-10: 1-931615-18-7
Printed in the United States

10 9 8 7 6 5 4 3 2 1

As a music, movement and drama teacher for 25 years, Carol Stock Kranowitz observed many out-of-sync preschoolers. To help them become more competent in their work and play, she began to study sensory integration theory. She learned to help identify their needs and to steer them into early intervention. In her workshops and writings for parents, educators, and other early childhood professionals, she explains how sensory difficulties play out—and provides practical and enjoyable techniques for addressing sensory issues at home and school.

Her publications include *The Out-of-Sync Child: Recognizing and Coping with Sensory Processing Disorder*, 2nd edition (Perigee, 2005) and *The Out-of-Sync Child Has Fun* (Perigee, 2003). *The Goodenoughs Get in Sync* (Sensory Resources, 2004), an illustrated children's book, tells the story of five family members and their naughty dog, each with a different sensory processing challenge. *The Goodenoughs* is an i-Parenting Media Award Winner and was named a Book-of-the-Year Finalist by *ForeWord Magazine* in the juvenile non-fiction category.

Carol also wrote *101 Activities for Kids in Tight Spaces* (St. Martin's, 1995). She co-authored *Hear, See, Play! Music Discovery Activities for Preschoolers* (Peg Hoenack's MusicWorks, 1989), the *Balzer-Martin Preschool Screening* (St. Columba's, 1992), and *Answers to Questions Teachers Ask about Sensory Integration* (Sensory Resources, 2001). Her articles on sensory processing, child development and preschool curricula have been published by *Parenting* magazine, *Family Circle*, and *Child Care Information Exchange* (www.ccie.com) and on Internet websites including www.SPDnetwork.org and www.child.com. She is the Editor-in-Chief of *S.I. Focus*, the international magazine dedicated to addressing sensory difficulties and improving sensory integration (www.SIFocus.com).

Carol earned a B.A. in English from Barnard College and an M.A. in education and human development from The George Washington University. She lives in Bethesda, MD, and has two sons and daughters-in-law and four wonderful grandchildren.

Many marvelous colleagues have contributed to making *Preschool SENSE* a reality. I am in debt to them all.

First, my most profound gratitude goes to Lucy Jane Miller, PhD, OTR, whose idea this was. One hot summer day in 2003, as we rested beside a dancing waterfall in the Colorado Rockies, she galvanized me to design this tool. She explained that not only parents and teachers could benefit from my "teacherly" viewpoint, but also occupational therapists could use a preschool educator's insights to help early childhood teachers recognize and address SPD in their students. Lucy, this is for you.

Second, my abiding appreciation goes to the late A. Jean Ayres, PhD, OTR, who set the stage for all of us devoted to fostering healthy sensory processing in young children.

Third, my thanks and devotion to these professionals are boundless:

Occupational Therapists: Patti Robbins and Janet Wright-Stafford, two other guiding lights who helped me see clearly and stay on track; as well as Marian Brice; Diana Henry; Jane Koomar, PhD; and Teresa A. May-Benson, PhD

Speech-Language Pathologist: Kathleen Morris

Early Childhood Educators and Special Educators: Karen Strimple, Heidi Cornnell, Laura Long, Linda Smith and Marie Walsh at St. Columba's Nursery School; and Julia Berry, Cheryl Geiger, Susan Snell, and Linda G. Barton.

Sensory Resources' Managing Directors: Polly A. McGlew and David E. Brown

Fourth, I thank many others who have influenced my thinking in fundamental ways, including these extraordinary therapists and educators: Marie Anzalone, Paula Aquilla, Lynn Balzer-Martin, Linda Barton, Barbara Bassin, Mary Benbow, Erna Blanche, Anita Bundy, Sharon Cermak, Sanford Cohen, Ellen Cohn, Georgia DeGangi, Kelly Dorfman, Winnie Dunn, Anne Fisher, Sheila Frick, Kimberly Geary, Laura Glaser, Tara Glennon, Stanley Greenspan, Elizabeth Haber, Barbara Hanft, Joanne Hanson, Melanie Hawke, Jane Healy, Margot Heiniger-White, Debi Wilson-Heiberger, Sharon Heller, Lois Hickman, Catherine Hostetler, Lynne Israel, Genevieve Jereb, Mary Kawar, Lorna Jean King, Linda King-Thomas, Nancy Kashman, Moya Kinnealey, Teri Kozlowski, Aubrey Lande, Shelly Lane, Marci Laurel, Barbara Lindner, Zoe Mailloux, Betty McBride, Heather Miller-Kuhaneck, Janet Mora, Myania Moses, Carolyn Murray-Slutsky, Elizabeth Murray, Joye Newman, Patricia Oetter, Beth Osten, Diane Parham, Betty Paris, Judith Reisman, Kathleen Resnik, Eileen Richter, Susanne Smith Roley, Laura Sopeth, Deanna Sava, Roseann Schaaf, Nancy Scheiner, Sherry Shellenberger, Larry Silver, Jill Spokojny Guz, Shirley Sutton, Stacey Szklut, Jenefer Tirella, Maryann Trott, Trude Turnquist, Sandy Wainman, Rondalyn Whitney, Christine Wittle, Julia Wilbarger, Patricia Wilbarger, Sue Wilkinson, Susan Windeck, Mary Sue Williams, and Ellen Yack

Fifth, I am beholden to the children who teach me that behavior means something, and that when we professionals scan it thoughtfully, compare notes, and work together, we can make some sense out of it.

Carol S. Kranowitz
Bethesda, Maryland, 2005

What is sensory processing? What is Sensory Processing Disorder (SPD), and how does it affect preschoolers' work and play? Early childhood educators became aware of these questions in 1998, when the first edition of *The Out-of-Sync Child* (Perigee) was published. The author, a preschool music and movement teacher for 25 years, wrote about this neurological problem in a jargon-free way that parents, educators, and other nontherapists could understand.

Revised in 2005, the book explains that some children withdraw from physical contact, refuse to participate in typical classroom and playground activities that their peers enjoy, or respond in an unusual way to ordinary sensations of touch, movement, sights, and sounds. These children don't behave as we expect – not because they WON'T, but because they CAN'T. Inefficient processing of sensory messages that come from their body and surroundings often causes their out-of-sync behavior.

To identify preschoolers who may have SPD, educators need a tool that speaks "teacher-ese" and focuses on specific, everyday sensory experiences at preschool. *Preschool SENSE* was developed to answer that need.

Purpose and Uses

Preschool SENSE is designed to facilitate communication between preschool educators and occupational, physical, and speech-language therapists. It is an educational tool to introduce early childhood teachers to Sensory Processing Disorder (SPD) – also known as Dysfunction in Sensory Integration (DSI).

Preschool SENSE is not an assessment, and it is not based on data or "standardized" on a normative sample of children. It is a scan intended to provide a quick glimpse of children (about 2 1/2 to 5 years of age) who may benefit from the therapist's skill to improve learning and behavior. It is intended to complement but not replace more thorough assessments, some of which are listed in this Manual.

For therapists, *Preschool SENSE* provides a framework for designing a collaborative, informal program for preschool teachers to use to help children with sensory problems that affect school performance. For educators, it provides easy-to-use checklists to record their observations about children who may show signs of sensory processing difficulties.

A preschooler whose Individual Child's Checklist suggests sensory processing problems should receive a comprehensive assessment by a pediatric occupational therapist with training in identifying SPD and interpreting assessment results. A complete diagnostic evaluation is essential, as *Preschool SENSE* must not be used as the sole basis for referring children for treatment.

Rationale for Screening Preschoolers

Children's sensory processing problems are often first noticed and recognized after the age of two years, when children arrive at preschool. Early intervention is key to treating these problems before they interfere with children's learning and behavior. Children respond most favorably to early intervention when their brains are developing rapidly and their neurological systems are most malleable.

Preschool educators play an important role in children's development and are in an excellent position to observe difficulties children may encounter in performing everyday tasks. Enlisting the aid of professional educators in recognizing children with sensory disorders enables therapists to concentrate their efforts on intervention for children who are most at risk.

Rationale for Development of *Preschool SENSE*

The reasons to identify and treat preschoolers with Sensory Processing Disorder are numerous, but "teacher-friendly" tools for collaborating with preschool educators are scarce. Educators may be unfamiliar with SPD and not understand what behaviors are associated with the disorder and what strategies to use at school to help the child. *Preschool SENSE* is intended to fill the void and put a practical and easy-to-use tool into teachers' hands.

Starting with *Preschool SENSE,* early childhood educators and occupational therapists can collaborate to identify children who should be tested with a comprehensive assessment, such as the *Miller Assessment for Preschoolers* (MAP, 1988, 1982) by Lucy Jane Miller, PhD, OTR; the *Sensory Processing Measure (SPM): School and Home Forms* (in press) by Heather Miller-Kuhaneck, OTR/L, Diana A. Henry, OTR/L, and Tara J. Glennon, EdD, OTR/L; and the *Sensory Profile School Companion* (in press) by Winnie Dunn, PhD, OTR.

Organization and Content of *Preschool SENSE*

Preschool SENSE has three parts:

* Materials for occupational therapists to direct the program

* Materials for educators to participate in the program

* Reference materials for occupational therapists and educators to share

All materials in this manual are reproducible, as described on the reverse of the title page, with the exception of three items: A Sense of This Child, A Sense of My Whole Class at Work and Play, and the Individual Child's Checklist. Samples of these three forms are included in this manual and blank copies are included in the *Forms Packet for Preschool SENSE.* See page 2 for additional information regarding the *Forms Packet.*

Materials for Occupational Therapists to Direct the Program

Six items are intended to help therapists direct the program:

1. Introductory Letter to Occupational Therapists from the Author

Written by the author, an experienced preschool teacher, this letter presents reasons that educators may not be "in sync" with occupational therapy consultants. The letter includes a list of questions to ponder as the therapist educates teachers about SPD and the importance of identifying preschoolers to "catch them before they fall" through the educational cracks.

2. *Preschool SENSE* Sequence

This provides the chronological order for directing the program.

3. Introductory Letter and Permission Form to Parents

This tells the parents or guardians that *Preschool SENSE* is going to occur at school. Parents are asked to complete and return the permission form for their children to be observed. This form is included in the *Forms Packet for Preschool SENSE.*

4. Selected Assessment Tools

This list, compiled with the help of Lucy Jane Miller, PhD, OTR, and Janet Wright-Stafford, OTR/L, includes some of the assessment programs that have been found to be useful in thoroughly evaluating preschoolers' skills.

5. Sensory Strategies for Classroom and Playground

This item is a sheet for the therapist to individualize for each child identified with SPD. The sheet suggests classroom modifications and sensory-motor activities that will benefit the particular child. When that child is helped, so is everybody else in the preschool classroom. This form is included in the *Forms Packet for Preschool SENSE.*

6. Follow-up Letter to Parents

This informs the parents that *Preschool SENSE* has been completed, and that the families of children who may have SPD will be contacted to discuss further options. This form is included in the *Forms Packet for Preschool SENSE.*

Materials for Educators to Participate in the Program

Five items are included for the educator:

1. Introductory Letter to Educators from the Author

This teacher-to-teacher letter welcomes educators to participate in the program.

2. Educator's Instructions for Participating in *Preschool SENSE*

This explains what the teacher is to do in the program, with a list of do's and don'ts. The therapist may copy this under her own letterhead, sign it, and give a copy to each participating teacher.

3. Questionnaire: A Sense of This Child

This two-page questionnaire asks the teacher to comment about the strengths and weaknesses of a particular student whose behavior is problematic in the classroom and on the playground. This preliminary questionnaire is designed to help the teacher focus on atypical patterns of behavior and to understand that inefficient sensory processing may be the underlying cause of a child's problems. The team determines which children to consider. This form is included in the *Forms Packet for Preschool SENSE.*

Providing several questionnaires to each teacher is recommended. After answering the questions for one child and understanding that sensory processing determines children's ability to play and learn, the teacher may want to consider several other children with puzzling behavior.

After completing the questionnaires, the educator meets with the therapist and other team members to determine which children to observe. Together, they may decide to consider:

- All the children in the class, whether or not they exhibit sensory difficulties, or
- Several children with observable sensory challenges, or
- One child who concerns the teacher but has not yet been identified, or
- One child whom has already been identified as having some school-related problems and about whom the teachers want to learn more.

The educator's answers on a questionnaire may suggest that a particular child's problem is other than SPD. In that case, the team may want to explore another possible cause of the child's atypical behavior, such as ADHD; an emotional problem; or a visual, hearing, or speech-language disability. They can then try another approach to help the child succeed at school.

4. Individual Child's Checklist

If the educator and therapist deem that the child does appear to have sensory processing issues, the educator proceeds to complete the four-page Individual Child's Checklist. This form is included in the *Forms Packet for Preschool SENSE,* and provides information about the development of the child's specific sensory processing abilities:

- Sensory Modulation Abilities

  The educator considers how the child modulates, or regulates, common sensory experiences at school in the sensory domains of touch, internal body works, movement and balance, body position and muscles, vision, hearing, smell, and taste. The educator checks whether the child:

  - Responds typically, as if saying, "This is okay!" or
  - Overresponds and avoids sensations, saying, "Oh, no!, or

- Underresponds and disregards sensations, saying, "Ho, hum," or
- Craves extra sensation, seeking sensory input and saying, "More!"
- Sensory Discrimination Abilities

The educator considers whether the child can discriminate among and between stimuli in the same sensory domains listed above. The educator checks whether the child:

- Responds typically, as if saying, "Aha!" or
- Responds atypically, without discerning differences, saying, "Huh?"
- Sensory-Based Motor Abilities

The first part of this section concerns postural responses, which allow a child to stabilize the body while moving or resting in response to the sensory demands of the environment or task. The educator considers whether the child can perform ordinary tasks expected of preschoolers using the sensory-based motor abilities of muscle tone, motor control, balance, bilateral coordination, unilateral coordination, and crossing the midline. The educator checks whether the child:

- Responds typically, saying, "I'm ready!" or
- Responds atypically and resists certain motor activities, saying, "Don't want to."

The second part of this section concerns praxis, which involves thinking of an idea for a new and multi-step action, planning the necessary moves, and carrying out the plan. The educator considers whether the child has developed adequate sensory-based abilities for gross-motor, fine-motor, eye-motor, and oral-motor activities and speech. The educator checks whether the child:

- Responds typically, saying, "I can do this," or
- Responds atypically, in a poorly coordinated manner, saying, "I can't do that."

5. A Sense of My Whole Class at Work and Play

The observable activities on this optional checklist for the educator matches the Individual Child's Checklist and helps the teacher collect data quickly while observing students engaging in ordinary group experiences. It is for the teacher's own use. The teacher does not turn it in. The teacher will need a set for every eight students. Thus, if a class has 16 children, the teacher needs two sets.

Reference Materials for Occupational Therapists and Preschool Educators to Share

Five items are offered for occupational therapists and teachers to share. Permission is granted for the following items to be photocopied for noncommercial use in the school as described on the reverse of the title page.

1. Taxonomy: Typical Sensory Processing and Sensory Processing Disorder

This shows the system of terminology used for the categories and subtypes of sensory processing disorder.

2. Common Behaviors of Preschoolers with and without Sensory Processing Disorder

These are detailed charts listing children's characteristic responses to ordinary sensory experiences at school. Side-by-side columns show the responses of typical children without SPD and of children with a **sensory modulation disorder**, a **sensory discrimination disorder**, or problems with **sensory-based motor abilities**.

In the examples of how SPD plays out, you will see the pronouns "he, him, his" more often than "she, her, hers," because most children identified with SPD are boys. (Many girls have SPD, too. They are less often identified, however, because their difficulties are less obvious.) Please understand that the out-of-sync behaviors illustrated in the examples apply to both boys and girls, whether the pronoun is male or female.

The examples illustrate symptoms that teachers see at school. That is the reason you will not see references to at-home activities (baths and shampoos, bedtime routines, and picky eating at dinner time) or out-and-about experiences (traveling in cars and airplanes, picnics and vacations, visiting relatives, and birthday parties).

The examples illustrate symptoms that teachers see in preschoolers. References to school experiences of older children, such as handwriting, lining up columns of numbers, copying from the blackboard, using a locker, and handing in homework will be in the forthcoming *Elementary SENSE*.

The author's 25 years of experience as a preschool teacher was at one school on the east coast in a middle-class, metropolitan area on the 39° latitude with an enormous, well-equipped playground, a traditional curriculum, and all kinds of weather. Please generalize the examples of preschoolers at work and play, if they do not jibe exactly with the experiences at your school.

3. Selected Therapies

This list has information about different kinds of treatment for children experiencing difficulties at school. A child may have a problem other than SPD. If so, one of these therapies may be able to address it.

4. Glossary

This includes definitions of terms used in *Preschool SENSE*.

5. Selected Bibliography

This is a list of publications to help therapists and educators learn more about SPD in young schoolchildren and how to help them at school.

User Qualifications

Preschool SENSE is designed for occupational therapists and other therapists with training and expertise in identifying Sensory Processing Disorder and in interpreting assessment results. Caution: Using this tool without a qualified therapist may lead to incorrect results.

Educators and classroom aides who fill out the questionnaire and checklist should have worked with the children in their care for at least one month, both indoors and out. They should be familiar with the child's abilities to use classroom materials, move on the playground and equipment, listen and learn, and relate to adults and other children.

Development of *Preschool SENSE*

Preschool SENSE was developed to make information about Sensory Processing Disorder accessible for preschool educators and classroom aides. It was developed, as well, to be an easy-to-use tool for observing children's developmental abilities in a preschool setting.

The questions selected for inclusion in this version are in simple language with no jargon and refer to behaviors that educators are almost certain to observe at preschool.

Administration of *Preschool SENSE*

Preschool SENSE is designed to be administered in the order listed on page 17. After the therapist has introduced the program, the teachers fill out the questionnaire A Sense of This Child (on page 31 and in the *Forms Packet*) and the Individual Child's Checklist (on page 33 and in the *Forms Packet*). Team teachers may confer with each other on their answers, as they each may see one child in a different light. A child's behavior often changes depending on the sensory challenges in environment, on who is with the child, on the materials being used, on whether the child is indoors or outside, and so forth. Sometimes these changes in behavior will indicate an underlying sensory problem. For instance, one teacher may see the child as avoiding messy play, while the coteacher may see the same child as not having a problem with messy play. Why the difference? Because the first teacher sets up art projects using smelly glue and paint, which irritate the child's oversensitive olfactory system, while the second teacher provides cinnamon-flavored playdough, which pleases the child.

The educators' instructions are to observe children's responses to sensory experiences. That is all. No room rearrangement, no complicated activities to set up, no strange person to visit in an empty classroom, and no unusual circumstances are required. The child should be observed in the most comfortable and familiar setting. The point is to scan the child's everyday abilities in everyday surroundings. Observations may extend over several days.

Do's and Don'ts

While educators fill out the questionnaire A Sense of This Child and the Individual Child's Checklist, here are their Do's and Don'ts:

- Do watch children carefully, particularly while they participate in group activities
- Do offer, if possible, the sensory experiences that are on the Checklist, such as a Feely Box, or a balloon toss
- Do call children's attention to new sensory experiences, such as curry powder on popcorn
- Do demonstrate how to do a task, such as open a snack package, if necessary, and then observe how the child attempts to do the job independently
- Do praise or thank children for trying, e.g., "I can see you don't like the way curry powder smells. That's ok. Thanks for giving it a sniff."
- Do not ever force a child to partake in a sensory experience that makes the child uncomfortable
- Do not have children rehearse or practice activities that are being observed
- Do not try to diagnose the child

The therapist collects the questionnaires and checklists by a specified date and proceeds to interpret them.

Interpretation of *Preschool SENSE*

Because *Preschool SENSE* is not a standardized instrument, consulting therapists must use their judgment to interpret the educator's checkmarks on each Individual Child's Checklist. The teacher's observations will reflect her knowledge of the child and the child's reactions to sensory stimuli under varying conditions. While reviewing those observations, the therapist should use her own training and experience to identify areas that may warrant therapeutic assessment using appropriate tools.

This tool is to be used not in lieu of other assessment instruments but in conjunction with them.

Dear Occupational Therapists,

This tool is designed to help you support early childhood teachers as they learn about Sensory Processing Disorder (SPD). With your guidance, the teachers will look at their 3-to-5-year-old students in a new light, with an eye for the children's sensory processing abilities as well as their sensory processing difficulties.

Getting started, however, may be a challenge. You may have found that teachers have reservations, at first, about the subject of sensory processing. Understanding these reservations and honoring each teacher's needs will make it easier for you to begin your partnership.

Reasons that Teachers May Not Be "In Sync" with Occupational Therapy Consultants

Their Attitude about Children with Sensory Differences or Difficulties

Teachers may

- Dislike or be exasperated by children with Sensory Processing Disorder (SPD)
- Believe that children will "just grow out of it"
- Feel that reaching and teaching these children is hopeless
- Have insufficient time to meet children's individual needs

Their Teaching Philosophy

Teachers may

- Believe the curriculum they have developed ain't broke – so why fix it?
- Feel that movement is nonacademic and thus superfluous
- Feel obligated to teach ABCs and reading readiness and to meet curriculum demands

Their Inexperience with Sensory Processing/Sensory Integration

Teachers may

- Be uneducated about the underlying reasons for atypical behavior in general
- Not understand what sensory processing/sensory integration (SI) is
- Not have worked before with an occupational therapist
- Not have witnessed the benefits of sensory-motor activities or sensory integration techniques at school
- Not grasp the educational relevance of sensory integration techniques to improve children's learning
- Want to incorporate sensory strategies but not know how to begin

Their Insecurity

Teachers may

- Resent advice from a visiting OT or other professional
- Worry about the reaction of parents to "bad news" about their child
- Fear losing control of an active group
- Fear they will do something wrong, harm the children, and get in trouble
- Fear they are being asked to "be therapists" and/or to "do therapy"

Their Constraints

Teachers may

- Feel that time, space and equipment are insufficient
- Feel that addressing their students' sensory needs is just "one more thing" they need to do
- Feel unsupported and fear that they will have to address sensory processing problems on their own
- Have their own sensory issues that preclude messy play, noisy fun, vigorous movement, and active engagement in the environment

In-Service Training

Getting in sync with educators means getting to know them. If possible, present an in-service training session to the teaching staff or meet with teachers individually to introduce them to the broad concept of SPD and OT/SI and to get them "in sync." At the training:

- Distribute the photocopied materials from the Manual to familiarize them with *Preschool SENSE*.
- Offer other handouts, articles, research papers, videos, and CDs (for suggestions, see the Selected Bibliography on page 64).
- Explain how identifying sensory problems in a few children and making minor changes in the classroom and routine may improve everyone's learning and behavior.
- Demonstrate the benefits of OT/SI by having teachers participate in activities that are
  - S.A.F.E. (Sensory-motor, Appropriate, Fun, and Easy to set up)
  - Educationally relevant
  - Thematic
  - Functional
  - Ideal for weaving into the early childhood curriculum

For suggestions, see

> *The Out-of-Sync Child Has Fun: Activities for Kids with Sensory Integration Dysfunction*, Perigee, 2003
>
> *The Goodenoughs Get in Sync: A Story for Kids about Sensory Processing Disorder*, Sensory Resources, 2004
>
> *101 Activities for Kids in Tight Spaces*, St. Martin's, 1995

- Emphasize that sensory-motor experiences help every one of us, by
  - Raising our energy level, in a positive way,
  - Helping us become organized and calm,
  - Improving our attention, and
  - Making our brains available for learning.

Partnerships

Develop partnerships with teachers by visiting the school, informally "hanging out" with them on the playground, and honoring their teaching and learning styles. Once the teachers understand the reasons for their students' challenging behavior, their reservations may vanish. Their "teacherly" observations will help determine the underlying causes of a child's atypical behavior, will help you and other professionals guide the family toward intervention, if needed, and will help the teachers make effective changes in their classrooms.

As you develop a partnership with teachers, you may want to get a sense of their teaching approach. Understanding how they feel about school life will help you fine-tune your recommendations. When teachers feel that you have "good vibrations," that you appreciate their skills, that you empathize with how challenging their job is, and see that you have composed a list of activities to harmonize with their particular classroom, they may be more willing to play along.

> Example: You want to provide extra sensory input for an underresponsive child. A teacher with tactile overresponsivity may ignore your suggestion of fingerpainting or other messy play activities. The same teacher may welcome, instead, a recommendation for "People Sandwich" and other experiences that incorporate deep pressure and don't make a mess.

> Example: You want to improve a child's visual-motor integration and suggest one-on-one activities, such as hole punching and lacing beads, to do every morning. A teacher with eight children with special needs may have no time to work exclusively with one child. Instead, the teacher may welcome a list of eye-hand experiences that all the children can enjoy, such as going on a peanut hunt.

Formally consult with educators and other school team members to determine which children to observe. You may decide to consider:

- All the children, whether or not they exhibit sensory difficulties, or
- Several children with observable sensory challenges, or
- One child who concerns the teacher but has not yet been identified, or
- One child whom has already been identified as having some learning disabilities and about whom the teachers want to learn more.

Collaborating will take time as you learn to merge your areas of expertise. Below are some questions to ponder while you get in sync.

What Is the Educator's Teaching Approach?

Classroom

How important are organization and neatness in the classroom?

How much space is in the room for active play and moving around?

Does the room have a quiet corner for children to "get away from it all"?

Curriculum

Does the teacher adhere to a formal curriculum or design it day by day?

Does the teacher run a structured or relaxed circle time, show and tell, and snack time?

Does the teacher encourage painting and art projects, science experiments and exploring nature, and messy play in a water table?

Does the teacher provide small manipulatives and promote fine-motor activities?

Does the teacher include activities for visual-motor integration?

Does the teacher enjoy singing, music and movement activities, rhythms and rhymes?

Does the teacher emphasize books and reading-readiness activities?

Does the teacher feel it is important for preschoolers to develop computer skills?

Teaching Style

Does the teacher give firm discipline and time-outs?

Does the teacher have a predictable or relaxed routine?

Does the teacher take frequent movement breaks (activity songs, stretching)?

Does the teacher show children how to use materials and do things ("guided discovery")?

Does the teacher let children explore materials and do things in their own way?

Does the teacher let children decide what activities to do and how long to stick with them?

Playground or Gym Time

How long is playground time or recess?

How important are gross-motor activities (digging, running, climbing, swinging)?

How important is messy play with sand, soil, water, snow, puddles, mud, paint, or bugs?

Does the teacher interact with children on the playground?

Students' Behavior

Does the teacher expect children to attend to activities they like for for 3-5 minutes (or longer)?

Does the teacher expect preschoolers to sit quietly for long periods (10 minutes) at circle time or story time, even if the children seem disinterested?

Does the teacher encourage self-help skills (dressing, snack time, cleaning up, and toileting)?

Does the teacher expect children to work with all materials?

How important is it for children to try new snacks, new puzzles, and new activities?

How important is it for the children to communicate with adults and other children?

How important is children's respect for classmates and animals?

Teacher's Own Learning Style

How does the teacher accept constructive criticism and advice?

Before trying a new activity, would the teacher prefer to read about it, observe it, hear about it, watch a video about it, or have a hands-on experience with it?

Discussing the above questions may help you suggest Sensory Strategies for Preschool for the child that will be most fitting for both teacher and preschooler.

Thank you for directing this program. Your clinical expertise, together with the teachers' classroom expertise, supplies essential information for understanding the whole child.

Warmest regards,

Carol

Carol S. Kranowitz, M.A. in Education & Human Development
Preschool teacher at St. Columba's Nursery School in Washington, DC, 1976-2001
Bethesda, Maryland 2005

Preschool SENSE Sequence for the Consulting Therapist

What to Do	Items to Use
1. Contact the school where you are, or will be, a consultant, and offer to use this tool.	Sample of *Preschool SENSE* forms, starting on page 31
2. Make appropriate copies of materials for the educators who are likely to participate. Fill out specific information. Give the Introductory Letter and the Educator's Instructions to the school to hand out to participating teachers.	Introductory Letter to Educators from the Author, on page 27 Educator's Instructions for Participating in *Preschool SENSE*, on page 29 and in the *Forms Packet*
3. If possible, present a teacher-training session and distribute Reference Materials and any other publications that will be welcome and useful.	Taxonomy: Typical Sensory Processing and Sensory Processing Disorder (SPD), on page 41 Common Behaviors of Preschoolers with and without Sensory Processing Disorder, starting on page 43 Selected Therapies, on page 57 Glossary, on page 61 Handouts, articles, research papers, videos, and CDs suggested in Selected Bibliography, on page 64
4. Make copies and have the school distribute letters to parents or guardians. Collect signed Permission Forms.	Introductory Letter to Parents with Permission Form, on page 19 and in the *Forms Packet*
5. Consult with team to determine which children to consider.	
6. Distribute questionnaires for teachers to fill out. Collect completed questionnaires.	A Sense of This Child, on page 31 and in the *Forms Packet*
7. Give both checklists to teachers. Collect Individual Child's Checklists only.	Individual Child's Checklist, on page 33 and in the *Forms Packet* A Sense of My Whole Class at Work and Play, on page 37 and in the *Forms Packet*
8. Copy follow-up letter to parents onto your letterhead, and give to school to distribute.	Follow-up Letter to Parents, on page 25 and in the *Forms Packet*
9. Have director contact parents whose children may have SPD to discuss your findings.	
10. Consult with school team, parents, and child's family physician about treatment plan for each child with SPD or other problem.	
11. Offer referrals to a therapist or multi-disciplinary team for a full assessment, or offer your services, if appropriate.	Selected Assessment Tools, on page 21
12. Provide teachers with individualized suggestions for each child identified with SPD.	Sensory Strategies for Preschool, on page 23 and in the *Forms Packet*

Materials for the Occupational Therapist to Direct the Program

Introductory Letters to Parents/Guardians

Dear Parents/Guardians,

Children develop at different rates. Some preschoolers take longer than others to pedal a tricycle, pump on the swing, trace a circle in fingerpaint, sing "The Wheels on the Bus," and carry on long conversations. Some of these late bloomers may simply need more time to develop these skills. Other late bloomers may have difficulty processing sensory information about touch, movement, sight and sound. About 10% - 15% of children have this problem, which is often undetected or misdiagnosed.

In the next few weeks, I shall be helping your child's teachers look at the developmental skills of all the children in the class. This "look-see" is called *Preschool SENSE (SENsory Scan for Educators)*. It is a brief look, not an in-depth evaluation. Your child will be observed while playing and will not be asked to answer questions, perform tasks, or leave the group.

Our goal is to help all the children here be successful in the occupation of childhood. Their occupation is playing, relating to other children and adults, participating in ordinary preschool activities, and moving around easily. After identifying children who struggle with these abilities, the school director or I will get in touch with the parents to discuss their child's sensory processing difficulties. Early identification and early intervention is key to help children before they fall through the cracks.

Please fill out the Permission Form below and return it to the school by _____
If you have questions, please contact me. Thank you!   **[date]**

Sincerely,

_____
[name of consulting therapist]   **[today's date]**

(___) ____-_____   _____@_____
[phone]   **[e-mail address]**

- - - - - - - - - - - - - - - - - **[cut here]** - - - - - - - - - - - - -

Parent's Permission Form

I give permission for the teachers and other professionals at my child's school to observe my child _____, using the *Preschool SENsory Scan for Educators (Preschool SENSE)*.
[child's name]

_____   _____
[date]   **[parent or guardian's signature]**

(___) ____-_____   _____@_____
[phone]   **[e-mail address]**

Selected Assessment Tools

The evaluation instruments listed below are some of the tools available to therapists. (Thanks to Lucy Jane Miller, PhD, OTR, and Janet Wright-Stafford, OTR/L, for their suggestions.)

Adaptive Behavior Assessment System, 2nd edition (ABAS—II)
> by Patti Harrison and Thomas Oakland
> www.psychcorp.com

Evaluation of three general areas of adaptive behavior: conceptual, social, and practical. Available in Spanish. All ages.

Bayley Scales of Infant and Toddler Development, 3rd edition (Bayley – III)
> by Nancy Bayley, PhD
> www.psychcorp.com

Screening, monitoring, and reassessment of a child's capacities to determine if child is "on track" developmentally or if more comprehensive assessment is needed. Ages one month to 42 months.

Beery VMI (Developmental Test of Visual-Motor Integration), 5th edition (VMI – 5)
> by Keith E. Beery, PhD; Norman A. Buktenica; and Natasha A. Beery
> www.wpspublish.com

Screening for visual-motor deficits that can lead to learning and behavior problems. Ages 2 to 8 (and up).

DAP:IQ (Draw-A-Person Intellectual Ability Test for Children, Adolescents, and Adults)
> by Cecil R. Reynolds and Julia A. Hickman
> www.proedinc.com

Common set of scoring criteria to estimate intellectual ability from a human figure drawing. Ages 4 and up.

FirstSTEp™ (Screening Test for Evaluating Preschoolers), also available in Spanish as *PrimoPASO*
> by Lucy Jane Miller, PhD, OTR
> www.wpspublish.com

Short screening, ideal for identifying preschoolers who are at risk for developmental delays. Ages 2.9 to 6.2.

Leiter International Performance Scale—Revised (Leiter—R)
> by Gale H. Roid, PhD, and Lucy Jane Miller, PhD, OTR
> www3.parinc.com

Totally nonverbal test of intelligence and cognitive abilities. All ages, including preschoolers.

MAP (Miller Assessment for Preschoolers)
> by Lucy Jane Miller, PhD, OTR
> www.wpspublish.com

Short, comprehensive assessment instrument to help evaluate young children for mild to moderate developmental delays. Ages 2.9 to 5.8.

Miller Function & Participation Scales (M-FUN-PS)
> by Lucy Jane Miller, PhD, OTR
> www.psychcorp.com

Assessment tool to evaluate a child's performance in functional tasks needed to successfully participate in classroom and school activities, with an emphasis on motor skill performance. Ages 2.6 to 7.11.

Motor Free Visual Perceptual Test, Revised (MVPT – R)
> by Ronald Colarusso, EdD, & Donald Hammill, EdD
> www.theraproducts.com

Assessment test designed for use with children with learning, cognition, motor, or physical disabilities. Ages 4 to 11.11.

Sensory Processing Measure (SPM): School and Home Forms
> by Heather Miller-Kuhaneck; Diana A. Henry; & Tara J. Glennon, EdD
> www.wpspublish.com

Assessment of a schoolchild's sensory processing abilities and social participation. Grades K-6.

Sensory Profile School Companion
> by Winnie Dunn, PhD
> www.harcourtassessment.com

Assessment for school-based clinicians to evaluate a child's sensory processing skills and how these skills affect the child's classroom behavior and performance.

TIME (Toddler & Infant Motor Evaluation)
> by Lucy Jane Miller, PhD, OTR, and Gale H. Roid, PhD
> www.unl.edu/buros

Designed to be used for diagnostic, comprehensive assessment of children who are suspected to have motor delays or deviations, for the development of appropriate remediation programs and for treatment efficacy research. Ages four months to 3.5 years.

Vineland Adaptive Behavior Scales, 2nd Edition (Vineland – II)
> by Sara S. Sparrow, PhD; Domenic V. Cicchetti, PhD; & David A. Balla
> www.agsnet.com

A measure of personal and social skills of special needs populations, including individuals with mental retardation, autism spectrum disorder, Asperger's syndrome, developmental delays, and ADHD. Ages birth to adulthood.

Sensory Strategies for Preschool

_____   _____/_____   _____
[child's name]   **[teachers' names]**   **[date]**

Here is a list of activities that will help to develop this child's sensory-motor skills. The activities have been selected to fit well in the preschool classroom and to benefit children of all abilities. Many preschool teachers have discovered that adding sensory-motor activities throughout the day improves children's learning and behavior. If you have questions about any of these activities, please give me a call.

1. Touch activities:

2. Movement and balance activities:

3. Body position and stretch activities:

4. Visual activities:

5. Hearing activities:

6. Smelling and tasting activities:

7. Oral-motor activities:

8. Motor-planning activities:

9. Fine-motor activities:

10. Bilateral coordination activities:

Have fun!

_____
[consulting therapist's name]

Follow-up Letter to Parents/Guardians

Dear Parents/Guardians,

We have completed the *Preschool SENSE (SENsory Scan for Educators)*. Observing your children at work and play has taught us what they want to do, what they can do, and what they are working hard to do.

Every little person has the inner drive to succeed in the "occupation of childhood." The child's occupation includes socializing with other children, listening to teachers' instructions, tossing balls, swinging, climbing ladders, enjoying dress-ups, pretending, playing with sand or messy fingerpaint, and participating in other ordinary experiences of preschool life.

But some children must work a great deal harder than others in their occupation, because of Sensory Processing Disorder (SPD). This problem interferes with their ability to develop important everyday skills. These children may fall through the educational cracks.

The school director will contact the families of the children who may have SPD and who may benefit from further evaluation. Recognizing children's difficulties and treating them appropriately is the best way to help children become as competent as they can be.

Thank you for caring so much about the healthy development of your child.

Warm regards,

_____   Date: _____

Introductory Letter to Educators from the Author

Dear Preschool Teachers,

Do you have students who are difficult, picky, oversensitive, undersensitive, grabby, pushy, withdrawn, clumsy, easily frustrated, inattentive, fidgety—in other words, out-of-sync? Of course, you do!

While most children are out-of-sync some of the time, some children are out-of-sync most of the time. They may have Sensory Processing Disorder (SPD), interfering with the way they process sensations coming from their body and the world around them. SPD is a "hidden tax" that interferes with learning, playing, and communicating with others.

Perhaps you wish to become more skillful in reaching and teaching these challenging students. *Preschool Sensory Scan for Educators (SENSE)* will make your classroom life more rewarding. Your observations of how an out-of-sync child functions at school may help you:

- Understand that Sensory Processing Disorder (SPD) is a developmental, physical problem, not a matter of willfulness or lack of intelligence

- Understand how SPD may interfere with a child's ability to function well at school and to develop smooth movement and balance, fine-motor skills, visual and listening skills, and relationships with adults and other children

- Be mindful of the fact that these are good children who are trying their best in a confusing world

- Discern a child's unique pattern of out-of-sync behavior, which may be overresponsive or underresponsive to ordinary sensory stimulation

- Provide safe, appropriate sensory-motor experiences in the classroom that will benefit all the students

- Structure a calm and organized classroom

- Collaborate with parents, occupational therapists, and other professionals on a child's behalf

When identified with SPD, most children benefit from early intervention. Natural early intervention can happen at school simply by adding more playground time to the day, or making the classroom softer with cushions and full-spectrum light bulbs, or providing more sensory-motor activities. Clinical early intervention, such as Occupational Therapy utilizing a Sensory Integration framework (OT/SI), at a clinic or home, often improves the child's participation at school. Almost all intervention results in a better-organized child —and classroom.

Thank you for participating in this program. It will make a huge and positive difference for all your young students—and for you!

Warmest regards,

Carol

Carol S. Kranowitz, M.A. in Education & Human Development
Former preschool teacher, St. Columba's Nursery School (in Washington, DC), 1976-2001
Bethesda, Maryland, 2005

Educator's Instructions for Participating in *Preschool SENSE*

Dear Preschool Educator,

Thank you for participating in *Preschool SENSE*. Your input is extremely valuable. While you may not be an expert on sensory processing, you certainly have expertise in working with children. Here is what you need to do:

1. Read Introductory to Educators from the Author. This will explain what the program is all about.

2. Read Reference Materials about Sensory Processing Disorder, which I can provide.

3. Consult with members of the team about the children to observe.

4. For each child you will observe, fill out A Sense of This Child. This is a questionnaire about the strengths and weaknesses of a particular student whose behavior is problematic. The questionnaire may help you understand that sensory processing may be the underlying cause. Turn in the questionnaire by the specified date.

5. Consult with the team about whether the child(ren) may benefit from further observation.

6. Make notes on the three-page checklist, A Sense of My Whole Class at Work and Play. Each three-page set is for eight students, if your class has 16 students, you will need two sets. This optional chart is for your own use, and you do not need to hand it in. It matches the Individual Child's Checklist. It will help you collect data quickly, as you observe all your students simultaneously while they work and play in a group setting. You will see patterns of SPD stand out, and seeing these patterns will help you fill out the Individual Child's Checklists. Write in eight children's names in the spaces at the top of the pages. For each sensory experience, put a checkmark (✔) if the children's responses are typical. Note differences or difficulties with a brief comment.

7. Fill out the four-page Individual Child's Checklist – one per child. This provides information about the child's specific sensory processing difficulties. How a child responds to everyday sensory experiences can affect his behavior, learning skills, communication, and relationships. You may see patterns emerge that will help clarify the child's underlying problems. Turn in this checklist by the specified date. Then, we can plan strategies to help not only the individual child but also your whole classroom.

Instructions: Put a checkmark (✔) in the space under a heading that best describes the child's response to a sensory experience. Write in N/A (Not Applicable) if you have not had an opportunity to view this behavior.

Do's and Don'ts as You Fill Out the Individual Child's Checklist

- Do watch children carefully, particularly while they participate in group activities

- Do offer, if possible, the sensory experiences that are on the Checklist, such as a feely box or a balloon toss

- Do call children's attention to new sensory experiences, such as curry powder on popcorn

- Do demonstrate how to do a task, such as opening a snack package, if necessary, and then observe how the child attempts to do the job independently

- Do praise or thank children for trying, e.g., "I can see you don't like the way curry powder smells.

That's ok. Thanks for giving it a sniff."

- Do not ever force a child to partake in a sensory experience that makes the child uncomfortable
- Do not have children rehearse or practice activities that are being observed
- Do not try to diagnose the child

8. Consult with the school team about the best treatment plan for each child.

9. Incorporate suggestions noted on the individualized Sensory Strategies for Preschool. These are ideas for classroom modifications and sensory-motor activities that will benefit the particular child. When that child is helped, so is everybody else in your preschool classroom.

10. Let's collaborate fully. If you have questions, please contact me. Thank you!

Sincerely,

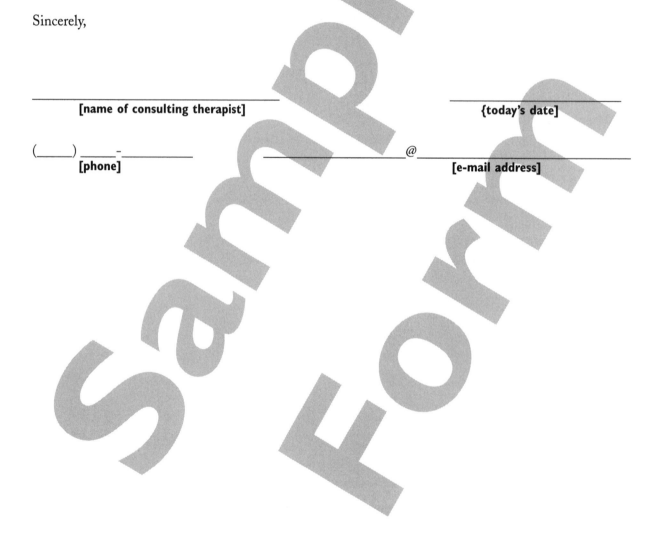

_____
[name of consulting therapist]

{today's date}

(_____) _____-_____

@_____

[phone]

[e-mail address]

A Sense of This Child

_____   _____   _____
       [child's name]   [teacher's name]   [date]

Dear Teacher,

Please think about this particular child's strengths and weaknesses. The child's behavior may be affected by sensory processing problems. Your observations will help us collaborate to come up with strategies to help the child function more smoothly at school.

1) What are this child's strengths? (Examples: Knows all about trains, remembers words to rhymes, sings well, is kind to smaller children, enjoys playground equipment, never tires, has many original ideas, etc.)

2) What are your primary concerns about this child? (Examples: Moves awkwardly and/or has difficulty with emotions, social participation, communication, attention, adapting to new situations or expectations, etc.)

3) What are some specific areas in which the child gets "stuck" and cannot seem to move on, change direction, or come up with a satisfactory response without assistance? (Examples: Getting out of the car, hanging up jacket, eating snack, talking with friends, recovering from being hurt, letting his needs and wants be known, staying in – or avoiding – one area of the room, etc.)

4) What are your priorities and goals for this child by the end of the school year? (Examples: Child will keep hands to himself, follow through with instructions, sit quietly for a table activity or story, ride a tricycle, try new snacks, stow items in his cubby, use all areas of the classroom, improve social skills, engage in conversations, play with several classmates, have a best friend, etc.)

5) How does this child respond to touching things and being touched? (Examples: Avoids messy play, jerks away from unexpected touch, overreacts to everyday jostling, craves messy play, enjoys roughhousing, etc.)

6) How does this child respond to moving and being moved? (Examples: Keeps feet on ground, is cautious and clumsy, bumps and crashes, spins and swings excessively, becomes frightened when pushed unexpectedly in chair or swing, etc.)

7) How well does this child perform self-help tasks? (Examples: Must work harder than other children to organize belongings, get dressed, open snack packages, use eating utensils, use bathroom, straighten clothes, etc.)

8) How does this child regulate his behavior? (Examples: Gets easily excited, tearful, or angry; has difficulty calming down and making transitions; cannot tolerate loud or unexpected noise; needs a jump-start to get going; is in constant motion; craves more of everything than other children, etc.)

9) How is this child's self-esteem? (Examples: Gets discouraged easily; refuses to try new experiences; says, "I'm no good at that," "I can't," "Nobody likes me," etc.)

10) Any other observations about the child's experiences and participation at school?

Best way for you to get in touch with me is

_____ Coming in to school at _____ o'clock

_____ Sending me an e-mail _____@_____

_____ Calling on the telephone (   ) _____

Mornings between _____ and _____ A.M., afternoons / evenings between _____ and _____ P.M.,
or Saturday / Sunday around _____ A.M. / P.M.

Individual Child's Checklist

Child's Name: _____ School: _____

Birth date: _____ Age: _____ years _____ months _____ Boy _____ Girl

Teacher(s): _____ / _____

Category 1: Sensory Modulation Abilities

(regulation of responses to sensory stimulation)

How do your students respond to these ordinary sensations? Put a checkmark (✔) in the space under a heading that best describes the child's response to a sensory experience. Write N/A if you have not seen this behavior.

Sense	In response to common sensory experiences at school, does this child...	Not an issue; Responds typically	Avoider: "Oh, no!" Overresponds	Disregarder: "Ho, hum." Underresponds	Craver: "More!" Seeks sensations
Touch	1. Avoid messy play or have a "meltdown" when touched by messy materials (sand, paint, glue, cookie dough, puddles)?			▓	▓
	2. Ignore sticky hands, disheveled clothes, and painful experiences (cuts, scrapes, slivers, stubbed toes, and bruises)?		▓		▓
	3. Seek personal body contact, unable to keep hands to self or to maintain personal space, and "all over" the other children?		▓	▓	
Internal body works	4. Complain of headache, stomachache, nausea, and "owies," and ask often for Band-Aids®?			▓	▓
	5. Not notice the need to urinate or to have a bowel movement?		▓		▓
	6. Seem constantly hungry, repeatedly asking, "When is snack?" and reaching for more to eat, even when snack is over?		▓	▓	
Movement and Balance	7. Become aggressive or fearful when moved unexpectedly (jostled or when chair is pushed)?			▓	▓
	8. Swing or spin for a long time without getting dizzy?		▓		▓
	9. Seek constant, active, intense movement (swinging or climbing high, jumping, spinning like a top, bouncing off things)?		▓	▓	
Body position and Muscles	10. Make excuses or complain of "growing pains" when expected to use muscles or joints for gross-motor activities?			▓	▓
	11. Object to or lack interest in pushing, pulling, lifting, carrying heavy loads or climbing stairs?		▓		▓
	12. Seek out bear hugs, bumping and crashing, and rough play?		▓	▓	
Vision	13. Wince in sudden, bright, or fluctuating light (sun through Venetian blinds, strong sunshine outdoors)?			▓	▓
	14. Not react when you flick classroom light on and off to get children's attention?		▓		▓
	15. Overfocus on novel visual stimulation (mobiles, moving people, and rolling balls)?		▓	▓	

Sense	In response to common sensory experiences at school, does this child...	Not an issue; Responds typically	Avoider: "Oh, no!" Overresponds	Disregarder: "Ho, hum." Underresponds	Craver: "More!" Seeks sensations
Hearing	16. Become easily bothered by loud, unexpected noise (fire alarm, shouting, doors closing, block structure tumbling down)?			█	█
	17. Appear unaffected by noisy places (crowded classroom, busy playground, school sing-a-long)?		█		█
	18. Make lots of noise over others' voices and sounds, bothering others when "good listening" is expected (circle time discussions, rhythm band, and other musical activities)?		█	█	
Smell	19. Complain about strong aromas (Crayons,® paint, cleaning products) and avoid using bathroom?			█	█
	20. Disregard strong aromas (cookies baking, cleaning products)?		█		█
	21. Sniff objects (doorknobs, toys, books, classmates, teachers and visitors)?		█	█	
Taste	22. As a picky eater, complain about or reject ordinary snacks that others enjoy?			█	█
	23. Disregard strong or unusual flavors (curry powder on popcorn, pumpkin pie)?		█		█
	24. Seek strong flavors (salt, salsa, garlic powder on popcorn)?		█	█	

Category 2: Sensory Discrimination Abilities

(distinguishing one sensation from another)

Sense	In response to common sensory experiences at school, can this child...	"Aha!" Usually	Jumbler: "Huh?" Rarely
Touch	25. Tell the difference between similar items she is touching without seeing them (pennies versus buttons in the feely box)?		
	26. Tell when face is dirty and needs wiping, or clothes are disheveled and need straightening?		
Internal body works	27. Identify area of body that hurts (stomachache, earache)?		
	28. Know to remove sweater when overheated, or to put on sweater when chilled?		
Movement and Balance	29. Move to protect self when about to fall?		
	30. Stop before having too much movement and before feeling nauseated (running, swinging, twirling)?		

Sense	In response to common sensory experiences at school, can this child...	"Aha!" Usually	Jumbler: "Huh?" Rarely
Body Position and Muscles	31. Position body parts correctly to get a job done (dressing; putting on boots; kicking a ball; or getting into unusual positions, such as being an "egg" or "tree")?		
	32. Use "just right" force on classroom tools (using brushes, Crayons®), on small toys (adjusting Transformers,® connecting Legos®), and with other children (roughhousing)?		
Vision	33. Locate picture or symbol in a group (finding self-portrait among others on bulletin board, or Waldo® on a busy page)?		
	34. Recognize an object regardless of its position in space (seeing that the upside-down jigsaw puzzle car piece will fit in the car place)?		
Hearing	35. Follow verbal directions without looking to others for visual cues?		
	36. Focus on your voice in a noisy classroom?		
Smell and Taste	37. Identify strong scents (scratch-and-sniff stickers, smelly markers, chocolate brownies)?		
	38. Identify when snacks are spicy, salty, sour, or sweet?		

Category 3: Sensory-Based Motor Abilities

Postural Responses (stabilizing the body while moving or resting in response to the sensory demands of the environment or task)

Sensory-Based Ability	Can This Child...	"I'm ready!" Usually	Slumper: "Don't want to." Rarely
Muscle tone	39. Be "at the ready" to react and move (participating in activity songs, such as "Clap, Clap, Clap Your Hands," or playing "Simon Says")?		
	40. "Hold on and stay put" (sitting on chair, swing, glider, or seesaw, or standing on merry-go-round, without falling off)?		
Motor control	41. Grasp and release objects successfully (cutting with scissors, picking up and placing jigsaw pieces)?		
	42. Bend and straighten joints smoothly (playing "up-down" games, such as growing like trees and falling like leaves)?		
Balance	43. Maintain balance while moving to different ground surfaces (stepping from car to sidewalk or from clatter bridge to sand)?		
	44. Maintain balance on playground equipment (sitting on swing, or walking on balance beam, railroad tie, or sandbox edge)?		
Bilateral coordination	45. Use both sides of body together (using rolling pin; doing the swimming, climbing, and rowing motions of the "Going on a Bear Hunt" game)?		
	46. Use one hand or foot to assist the other (pouring juice into cup, drawing and cutting paper, kicking a ball)?		

Sensory-Based Ability	Can This Child...	"I'm ready!" Usually	Slumper: "Don't want to." Rarely
Unilateral coordination	47. Reach out directly to retrieve object (block, pitcher, triangle)?		
	48. Manipulate small object with preferred hand (handling a counting bear, board game piece, or needle to lace beads)?		
Crossing the midline	49. Cross midline, i.e., use one eye, hand, or foot in space of other eye, hand, or foot (motioning like windshield wipers in "Wheels on the Bus," or kicking a ball diagonally)?		
	50. At the easel, paint a horizon from left to right with one hand?		

Category 3: Sensory-Based Motor Abilities

Praxis (thinking of an idea for a new, multi-step action, planning the necessary moves, and carrying out the plan)

Sensory-Based Skill	Can This Child...	"I can do this." Usually	Fumbler: "I can't do that." Rarely
Thinking, planning, and doing	51. Think of a new activity having several steps (putting on new firefighter costume and playing Firehouse)?		
	52. Think of different ways to use a simple object (string, hoop, scarf, block, paper towel tube?)		
Gross-motor	53. Maneuver body around crowded classroom and playground with good coordination (moving from swings to sandbox, playing "Red Light, Green Light," dancing to Hap Palmer's song about "Sammy")?		
	54. Mount and pedal new tricycle, scooter, or classroom ride-on toy?		
Fine-motor	55. Use classroom tools easily (using scissors or hole puncher, upending and squeezing glue bottle)?		
	56. Succeed at self-help tasks in classroom and on playground, such as dressing (snapping, zipping) and snack-time jobs (opening cracker packages)?		
Eye-motor	57. Follow a moving object (ball or balloon) with eyes in order to catch it?		
	58. Focus on near and far points (looking from peanut-butter-and-pinecone birdfeeder out the window to paintbrush in hand)?		
Oral-motor skills & Speech	59. Eat and chew normally, without excessive messiness?		
	60. Speak clearly enough to be understood by most people?		

A Sense of My Whole Class at Work and Play

Category 1: Sensory Modulation

How do your students respond to these ordinary sensations? Put a checkmark (✔) if responses are typical.
Note a difference or difficulty with a brief comment or "Oh, No," "Ho, hum," or "More!"

Children's Names →								
1. Messy play or being touched by messy item								
2. Sticky hands, bruises, disheveled clothes								
3. Personal body contact with other children								
4. Stomachache, earache, other internal pain								
5. Need to urinate or have bowel movement								
6. Hunger, snack time								
7. Being moved unexpectedly								
8. Dizziness after spinning								
9. Active, intense movement								
10. Using muscles for gross-motor play								
11. Pushing, pulling, lifting, carrying loads								
12. Bear hugs, rough play								
13. Sudden, bright light or sunshine								
14. Flickering classroom light								
15. Novel visual stimuli								
16. Loud, sudden noise								
17. Noisy environments								
18. Times requiring "good listening"								
19, 20, 21. Strong aromas								
22, 23, 24. Strong flavors								

Category 2: Sensory Discrimination

Can your students tell the difference between ordinary sensations? Put a checkmark (✔) if responses are usually typical or "Aha!" Note a difference or difficulty with a brief comment or "Huh?"

Children's Names →									
25. Tell difference between similar items he touches without seeing									
26. Tell when face or clothes are messy									
27. Identify area of body that hurts									
28. Remove / put on sweater when hot / cold									
29. Protect self when about to fall									
30. Stop before having too much movement									
31. Position limbs correctly to get dressed									
32. Use just right force on tools, toys, children									
33. Locate picture in a group									
34. Recognize object even if upside-down									
35. Follow directions without visual cues									
36. Focus on your voice in noisy classroom									
37. Identify strong scents									
38. Identify strong flavors									

Category 3: Postural Responses

Can your students make appropriate responses when changing their body position or using their muscles? Put a checkmark (✔) if responses are usually typical or "I'm ready!" Note a difference or difficulty with a comment, "Don't want to," or just "No."

39. Be "at the ready" to react and move									
40. "Hold on and stay put" on chair or swing									
41. Grasp and release objects									
42. Bend and straighten joints smoothly									
43. Maintain balance on different surfaces									
44. Maintain balance on playground equipment									

Children's Names →								
45. Use both sides of body together								
46. Use one hand or foot to assist the other								
47. Reach for object								
48. Manipulate small item with preferred hand								
49. Cross midline								
50. Paint left to right line								

Category 3: Praxis

Can your students think of a new, multi-step action, plan how to do it, and then carry out the plan? Put a checkmark (✔) if responses are usually typical or "I can do this." Note a difference or difficulty with a comment, "I can't do that," or "Can't."

51. Think of a new, multi-step action								
52. Think of different ways to use an object								
53. Move body smoothly through space								
54. Mount and ride new tricycle or ride-on toy								
55. Use classroom tools								
56. Do self-help tasks								
57. Follow a moving object with eyes								
58. Focus on near and far points								
59. Eat and chew without much messiness								
60. Speak clearly enough to be understood								

Taxonomy of SPD

In 2004, a distinguished group of occupational therapists and colleagues collaborated to update the terminology used in sensory integration. Their taxonomy is the one used in *Preschool SENSE*.

Lucy Jane Miller, PhD, OTR, FAOTA; Director, KID Foundation; Associate Professor, University of Colorado Health Sciences Center

Sharon A. Cermak, EdD, OTR, FAOTA; Professor, Boston University

Shelly J. Lane, PhD, OTR/L, FAOTA; Professor, Virginia Commonwealth University

Marie Anzalone, ScD, OTR, FAOTA; Assistant Professor, Columbia University

Jane Koomar, PhD, OTR/L, FAOTA; Director OTA-Watertown; President, Spiral Foundation

Beth Osten, OTR

Stanley I. Greenspan, MD

The typical preschooler has developed

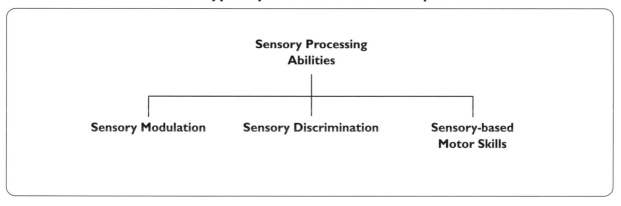

The atypical preschooler may have

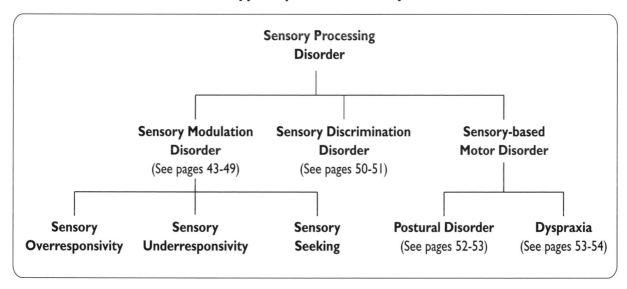

Common Behaviors of Preschoolers with and without Sensory Processing Disorder

Category 1: Sensory Modulation (regulation of responses to sensory stimulation)
The Tactile Sense (Touch)

Topic	Typical Child ("Okay!" on Individual Child's Checklist)	Sensory Avoider ("Oh, no!" on Individual Child's Checklist)	Sensory Disregarder ("Ho, hum" on Individual Child's Checklist)	Sensory Craver ("More!" on Individual Child's Checklist)
Light touch on skin and hair	Notices light, unexpected touch sensations on skin and hair, but is not bothered	Reacts negatively and emotionally to light touch sensations and/or to the possibility of these sensations	Does not notice light touch sensations on skin and hair, as when you touch her shoulder to get her attention	Asks for frequent back rubs and "tickles" on skin and palms of hands
		Curls or protects hands to avoid touch sensations		
		Reacts negatively when hair is touched by rain, sand, or mulch, or when hair is ruffled by breeze	Does not notice mussed hair, or mulch or sand in hair	May twirl hair in fingers
Feet	Walks barefoot on grass and sand	Resists walking barefoot on grass and sand	When barefoot, may not notice or complain about gravel, scratchy grass, hot tarmac, or stubbed toes	Walks barefoot on surfaces that others find uncomfortable, such as gravel or Legos,® to get extra input
		Walks on tiptoes (to avoid touch pressure on soles)		
	Has no problem wearing shoes and socks	Refuses to remove shoes		Frequently removes socks and shoes
Touching and handling objects	Likes to touch, handle, and explore toys, school materials, and equipment	Avoids touching, handling, and exploring new toys and materials that appeal to other children	Appears to lack desire to touch, handle, and explore toys and materials that appeal to other children	"Gotta touch" everything, even if it is inappropriate to handle
				Rubs and bites hands and skin
	Is comfortable touching people and objects with his hands	Avoids touching other people		Seeks to touch certain surfaces and textures that others find uncomfortable, e.g., pressing hands on tree bark
				Frequently switches activities to get novel touch sensations
Messy play	Enjoys messy play, such as fingerpainting, gluey art projects, sculpting in clay, and splashing in water	Avoids messy play and splashing in water, becoming tearful at idea	Is unaware of messiness on hands or face, not noticing sticky hands, a runny nose, or crumbs around mouth	Seeks frequent and intensely messy play and stays with it longer than most others
				Likes playing in puddles and snow more than other children
Weather	Tolerates bad weather conditions with rain, wind, or gnats	Becomes upset in weather with rain, wind, or gnats	Oblivious to weather conditions with wind, rain, or gnats	Loves going out in rain, having coat open in the wind

Topic	Typical Child ("Okay!")	Sensory Avoider ("Oh, no!")	Sensory Disregarder ("Ho, hum")	Sensory Craver ("More!")
Clothing	Tolerates stiff or scratchy clothes for brief periods, e.g., for a class performance or school party, or to try on dress-ups	Is fussy about clothing and footwear, shirt tags and sock seams, requiring all fabric textures to be soft and seamless	May not notice that clothes are in disarray, or that cuffs and socks are wet	
		Avoids lacy, scratchy dress-ups, synthetic materials, wool caps		
	Usually tolerates tags in tee-shirts and bumps in sock	Resists wearing—or removing—clothes and shoes		
		Wears jacket indoors; wears long pants even in hot weather		
Eating	Will try a bite of most new snacks with varying consistencies and textures	Is picky about consistency and texture of food, complaining about snack offerings and preferring a mushy, creamy, "white" diet (processed cheese, yogurt, milk, ice cream) or a crunchy, "brown" diet (toast, pretzels, chips) because of oral oversensitivity	Does not react to salty, spicy, or tart snacks	"Dives" into snacks, often cramming mouth full
Personal Contact	Moves away when others lean, push, or invade his body space	Avoids most physical contact with people, school pets, or objects	Does not move away when leaned on or crowded	Shows "in your face" behavior, getting very close to others and touching them, even if these touches are unwelcome
	Tolerates or enjoys affectionate pat on head, kisses, hugs			

Category 1: Sensory Modulation—Pain and Temperature

Topic	Typical Child ("Okay!")	Sensory Avoider ("Oh, no!")	Sensory Disregarder ("Ho, hum")	Sensory Craver ("More!")
Bruises & Pain	Responds to minor bruises or pain with mild complaint and then moves on	Excessively whines, cries or complains about a minor hurt, seeming to make a "mountain out of a molehill"	Does not notice pain or complain about a cut, scrape, sliver, bruise, or stubbed toe or about being squeezed too hard	Seeks experiences that may be painful to others, such as holding an icicle
	Responds to major pain with loud complaint, calming down, eventually	Sobs and suffers greatly and inconsolably over major hurts	May notice major pain but shrugs it off, perhaps ignoring a broken finger or collarbone	

Category 1: Sensory Modulation—Pain and Temperature (cont'd.)

Topic	Typical Child ("Okay!")	Sensory Avoider ("Oh, no!")	Sensory Disregarder ("Ho, hum")	Sensory Craver ("More!")
Heat & Cold	Tolerates very warm or cool classroom and weather	Complains about heat or cold, indoors and out	Does not notice heat, cold, or temperature changes, indoors or out, often keeping on jacket in hot weather or heated rooms, or refusing a jacket in cold weather	Likes very hot or chilly room temperature
	Adapts to temperature changes (moves out of sun or removes coat if hot; bundles up if cold)	Avoids outdoor play in summer or winter		Has high tolerance for sweltering summer or freezing winter weather
	Eats hot and cold snacks ("Stone Soup," ice cream)	Wants food to be luke-warm		Enjoys steamy hot and icy cold foods

Category 1: Sensory Modulation— Interoception (Internal body works)

Topic	Typical Child ("Okay!")	Sensory Avoider ("Oh, no!")	Sensory Disregarder ("Ho, hum")	Sensory Craver ("More!")
Internal body works	Feels hunger or thirst and welcomes food or drink	Is overly aware of somatic (bodily) perceptions and is bothered by them, such as hunger, stomach- or headache, or nausea	Does not notice hunger or thirst	Eats frequently and a lot, often asking, "When's snack?"
	Indicates need to use toilet or that he has a soiled diaper		Does not notice the need to urinate or move bowels; may be very late in toilet training and still have frequent "accidents"	Likes to generate internal sensations, such as burping

Category 1: Sensory Modulation—The Vestibular Sense
(Movement through space and change in head position)

Topic	Typical Child ("Okay!")	Sensory Avoider ("Oh, no!")	Sensory Disregarder ("Ho, hum")	Sensory Craver ("More!")
Passive movement (being moved)	Tolerates being moved, e.g., jostled in line, pushed on swing, or shoved in a chair – and easily regains balance	Becomes overly anxious, aggressive, or fearful when head is being moved, e.g., when pushed on swing	Does not seem to notice being moved on swing or jostled in line	Seeks to be pushed on swing longer than most other children, calling, "Higher! Higher!"
Active movement	Enjoys (for several minutes) intense movement, e.g., swinging, spinning on tire swing, or somersaulting	Avoids intense movement, such as swinging, turning and spinning, somersaulting, running, or sliding	Seems to lack desire to move actively	Seeks intense movement, enjoying spinning, sliding, fast-moving playground equipment for much longer than others
	Likes to experiment with different movement activities		Not a "self-starter"	Constantly moves, jiggles, rocks
				Is a thrill-seeker and takes more physical risks than others

Category I: Sensory Modulation—The Vestibular Sense (cont'd.)

Topic	Typical Child ("Okay!")	Sensory Avoider ("Oh, no!")	Sensory Disregarder ("Ho, hum")	Sensory Craver ("More!")
Head position	Nods and shakes head easily	Holds head in rigid position		Frequently nods, shakes, tilts head from side to side
	While standing on two feet, tilts or moves head freely in movement games: • Plays "Hokey Pokey" and "I'm a Little Teapot" • Moves like animals • Rolls like a log • Falls like an autumn leaf • Grows like a beanstalk	When standing on two feet, resists tilting head from side to side or looking over shoulders in movement games, preferring to keep head upright and eyes front or gazing up at ceiling or clouds		In movement games requiring different head positions, "goes overboard," tilting head farther off-center than other children do
		Becomes anxious when head is upside-down, as in somersault position		Seeks movement involving unusual positioning of head, such as hanging upside down from monkey bars, or swaying "tummy down" on a swing
Dizziness	Gets dizzy after spinning	Has significantly unpleasant reaction to movement, e.g., extreme dizziness, sweating, nausea, or rapid heart rate	Once started, spins for lengthy time and does not get dizzy	Seeks to spin for a long time and often does not feel dizzy
Heights & being off ground	Enjoys being off the ground, e.g.: • Crosses "Three Billy Goats Gruff" bridge • Walks on balance beam and ramps in obstacle courses • Climbs over monkey bars	Hates to let feet leave the ground	May move or take movement risks with no regard for safety, e.g., jumping from top of climbing gym	Climbs constantly and fearlessly, often scaling heights, such as the uppermost climbing gym rungs, that other children instinctively know are off limits
		Fears heights		
Falling	Notices sensation of falling, and extends foot or hands to break fall and protect himself	Has primal fear of falling and is extremely upset when he does fall	Does not notice sensation of falling and does not respond efficiently by extending hand or foot in self-protection	Enjoys falling, twirling, and crashing to the ground, like a downed helicopter

Category 1: Sensory Modulation—The Proprioceptive Sense
(Body position and muscle movement)

Topic	Typical Child ("Okay!")	Sensory Avoider ("Oh, no!")	Sensory Disregarder ("Ho, hum")	Sensory Craver ("More!")
Deep pressure to muscles and joints	Enjoys deep pressure on muscles and joints, e.g., being massaged or hugged tightly	Avoids deep pressure and may show anxiety when hugged tightly	Becomes more alert and organized after deep pressure input to muscles and skin, such as being hugged, massaged, or rolled on a mat like a hotdog	Craves strong bear hugs and being pressed, squeezed, or pummeled while roughhousing
				Throws himself to the ground, crashes onto gym mats, and lunges into leafpiles
				Bumps and crashes into people, objects in intrusive and objectionable way
				Clenches and grinds teeth, and bites and chews inedible things, e.g., collars, cuffs, and pencils
Active movement	Has inner drive to play active games using muscles, e.g., hopping on one foot, jumping rope, running, bouncing on trampoline, playing Tug-of-War, rolling, and crawling	Avoids jumping, hopping, running, crawling, rolling, and other playground activities involving muscles and joints, perhaps complaining of "growing pains"	Becomes more alert and organized after actively moving, although he needs more intense muscle stimulation than others in order to "get in gear" for play	Moves constantly, getting in and out of seat, stomping, jumping around
				Seeks intense playground activities using muscles, much more than other children
Heavy work	Actively participates in heavy work using the muscles, such as pushing, pulling, lifting and carrying heavy loads, and shoveling, digging, raking, sweeping	Does not enjoy pushing, pulling, lifting, carrying, or other heavy work activities	May object to pushing, pulling, lifting, carrying loads, climbing stairs, or using muscles in other heavy work activities	Seeks heavy work, i.e., pushing other kids on swings, pulling a loaded wagon, shoving furniture around, or carrying large bags of rabbit food

Category I: Sensory Modulation—The Proprioceptive Sense (cont'd.)

Topic	Typical Child ("Okay!")	Sensory Avoider ("Oh, no!")	Sensory Disregarder ("Ho, hum")	Sensory Craver ("More!")
Body position and body awareness	Enjoys getting into unusual positions, scrunching down to be an egg, stretching up like a tree, moving like animals, climbing through jungle gym bars	Resists getting into unusual positions	Cannot orient body to get into unusual positions	Sits in unusual positions, e.g., hugging knees under chin, or folding legs under buttocks while sitting on a chair
	Readjusts body position to do a task more efficiently, e.g., sits down to put on shoes, or shifts hands on shovel for a better grip	Is overly aware of body, but is rigid, tense, and uncoordinated	Lacking body awareness, does not notice body position or what body parts are doing	
	Moves body in coordinated way through space in the classroom and on the playground		Moves in uncoordinated way, bumps into other children, furniture, playground equipment	
	Stretches to "get the kinks out" after sitting still for a while		Does not notice discomfort of sitting in one position for long time	

Category I: Sensory Modulation—The Visual Sense (Vision)

Topic	Typical Child ("Okay!")	Sensory Avoider ("Oh, no!")	Sensory Disregarder ("Ho, hum")	Sensory Craver ("More!")
Visual stimulation	Notices novel visual stimuli and soon gets used to it	Is quickly overexcited by visual stimuli, such as dangling mobiles or people moving about, and has difficulty getting used to them	Does not pay attention to novel visual stimuli, such as holiday decorations or rearranged classroom furniture	Is attracted to and overfocuses on novel visual stimulation, such as mobiles, moving people, rolling balls, and computer screens
	Notices objects coming toward him, such as a ball or a child on a swing, and responds appropriately	Flinches when objects come toward him, such as a ball or another child moving fast	Does not respond efficiently when objects approach, e.g., when a ball is tossed directly to child	
Bright light	Blinks at or turns away from sudden, bright sunlight or flickering lights	Winces at sudden, bright lights and flickering overhead lights, often shielding eyes with hands, sunglasses, or caps with visors, even indoors	Does not seem to notice bright light or sun, flickering fluorescent bulbs, or when teacher flicks classroom lights to get children's attention	Is attracted to bright, flickering light, e.g., strobe lights or sunlight through Venetian blinds
Eye contact	Maintains direct eye contact	Avoids direct eye contact	Stares at faces or objects, "looking right through them," not seeming to see them	Stares for exceptionally long time at objects or people

Category 1: Sensory Modulation—The Auditory Sense (Hearing)

Topic	Typical Child ("Okay!")	Sensory Avoider ("Oh, no!")	Sensory Disregarder ("Ho, hum")	Sensory Craver ("More!")
Background sounds	Alerts initially to loud, unexpected noises, such as shouts, doors slamming, fire alarms and sirens, and then adapts to them	Reacts strongly and negatively to loud, unexpected noise, e.g., shouts, sirens, and slamming doors, and does not adapt to them	Becomes alert and "turns on" to extremely loud, close, or sudden voices or sounds (especially if sound is accompanied by another sensation such as a tactile or visual cue), e.g., doors slamming, toy trucks crashing, or block towers tumbling	Welcomes loud noises, preferring high volume on music player
	Alerts initially to quiet sounds, such as gerbils nibbling or soft music, and then ignores them	Alerts to quiet sounds and keeps attending to or complaining about them after others tune them out	Often does not respond to quiet sounds, soft voices and whispers, which may be "under his radar"	
	Notices and tolerates ordinary background noises, e.g., people talking, teacher calling kids' names, doors closing, and chairs scraping	Withdraws, covers ears with hands, and complains about ordinary sounds that do not bother others, e.g., toilets flushing or spoons clinking	Often does not respond to ordinary sounds, voices, questions, and comments	
Noisy places	Tolerates crowds and noisy places, e.g., school sing-a-longs	Withdraws from crowded and noisy places, covering ears	Seems oblivious to noisy places such as crowded classroom, busy playground, or school sing-a-long	Loves crowds and hubbub of noisy places
		Worries about potentially noisy places (e.g., the all-purpose room) and loud sounds (e.g., balloons that may pop)		
Child's own sounds	Modulates voice for the situation, i.e., uses conversational tone indoors and louder voice on the noisy playground	May speak very softly as surrounding noise increases	May speak very loudly and be unaware of volume of own voice	Raises voice beyond comfortable level for others, i.e., uses his "outside voice" in the classroom
				Creates own noises, bothering others
Musical activities	Enjoys singing, clapping, and rhythm band activities	Avoids loud noise-makers such as rhythm band instruments	Seems uninterested in rhythm band instruments and musical activities	Claps, sings, and plays rhythm band instruments extremely loudly and often out of rhythm

Category 1: Sensory Modulation—The Olfactory Sense (Smell) and the Gustatory Sense (Taste)

Topic	Typical Child ("Okay!")	Sensory Avoider ("Oh, no!")	Sensory Disregarder ("Ho, hum")	Sensory Craver ("More!")
Aromas	Inhales pleasant, strong aromas, such as cookies baking or honeysuckle	Avoids strong aromas, even pleasant ones	Does not notice strong or unusual aromas, or is not bothered by them	Seeks strong odors, such as paint, glue, and cleaning products
	Wrinkles nose, pinches nostrils, or moves away from unpleasant odors	Complains loudly about mild odors that do not bother others	Often cannot smell his food	Frequently sniffs food, people, and objects
		Avoids bathroom		
Flavors	Tolerates or enjoys unusual flavors	May gag when eating	Can eat very spicy snacks without reaction	Seeks strong, tart, hot, and spicy flavors, such as salsa and pickles
	Willingly tastes variety of new flavors	Is a picky eater and complains about snacks others enjoy		Licks and tastes inedible objects, such as play-dough, toys, furniture, doorknobs, people

Category 2: Sensory Discrimination (distinguishing one sensation from another, discerning specific qualities of a sensation, and giving meaning to sensory stimuli)

Sense	Typical Child ("Aha!" on Individual Child's Checklist)	Sensory Jumbler ("Huh?" on Individual Child's Checklist)
Tactile (Touch)	Knows when face is dirty or clothes are disheveled and tries to tidy up	Is unaware of shoes on wrong feet, sagging socks, untied shoelaces, twisted waistband, and untucked shirt
	Recognizes small objects just by feeling, such as small toys hidden in Feely Box or buried in sand table	Cannot distinguish hidden objects by touch alone without seeing them, such as small toy in pocket, Feely Box, or sand table
	Can feel the difference between similar items that he is touching, e.g., oatmeal cookie vs. cracker, sand vs. mud, crayon vs. marker	Cannot use touch alone to know the difference between similar items he is using, such as crayon vs. marker, or toy car vs. school bus
		Seems "out of touch" with hands, feet, and other body parts, as if they are unfamiliar attachments
Pain	Tells whether pain, such as a sore throat or stomachache, is lessening, worsening, or not changing	Has trouble telling whether pain is lessening, worsening, or staying the same
	Can indicate area of body that hurts	Has only a general sense of pain coming from body; cannot indicate location
Temperature	Can tell the difference between hot and cold, e.g., tap water, "Stone Soup"	Has trouble discerning heat, cold, or gradations in between, possibly scalding fingers in hot tap water or freezing fingers by playing in snow without mittens
	Knows to remove sweater when body is overheated and to put on sweater when body is chilled	Seems unaware of body temperature and does not know to remove sweater when overheated or to put on sweater when cold
Interoception (Internal body works)	Feels that he urgently needs to urinate or have a bowel movement, or that he can "hold it" for a few minutes	Does not feel when he needs to urinate or have a bowel movement

Category 2: Sensory Discrimination (cont'd.)

Sense	Typical Child ("Aha!" on Individual Child's Checklist)	Sensory Jumbler ("Huh?" on Individual Child's Checklist)
Vestibular	Sticks out hands or foot in protective extension to catch self when falling or about to fall	Falls frequently off seat or while moving or standing, unable to catch self
	Can change direction smoothly while moving on the playground or in the classroom	Becomes easily confused when turning, changing directions, going through obstacle courses, or playing games like "Go In and Out the Window" and "Duck, Duck, Goose," when head is not upright
	Enjoys games like "Pin the Tail on the Donkey" in which eyes are closed or covered	Is especially unsteady and resists moving when eyes are closed or covered, as in "Pin the Tail on the Donkey" or when wearing a Halloween mask
	Can tell whether head is outside the regular position, during activities such as "I'm a Little Teapot," rolling down the hill, or somersaulting	Can't tell whether position of head is upside down or tilted up, down, or to the side, during activities such as "I'm a Little Teapot" or rolling down the hill
	Stops swinging or twirling when she has had enough movement and before becoming too dizzy or sick	Cannot tell when she has had too much swinging, twirling, or other movement and keeps going, until she gets too dizzy or feels sick
Proprioceptive	Appears to be comfortable in own body	Appears to be uncomfortable or unfamiliar with own body, as if he has not yet "met" his arms, hands, legs and feet
	Positions limbs correctly for activity such as getting dressed, kicking a ball, and pedaling a tricycle	Has difficulty positioning arms and legs for activities such as putting on jacket, pants, and boots; kicking a ball, getting into and out of car; pedaling a tricycle
	Adjusts muscle movements smoothly when bending and straightening body parts to march, touch toes, climb stairs, or "fly"	Moves muscles in jerky manner when bending and straightening body parts to march, touch toes, climb stairs, or "fly like a bird"
	Adjusts muscles to lift a heavy box or bucket and carries it fairly smoothly	Has difficulty adjusting muscles for lifting, carrying, pushing, or pulling cartons, buckets, blocks, chairs, and lunch boxes
	Uses "just right" force (not too hard, not too loose) when using small manipulative toys	Uses not enough force or too much force when manipulating crayons, Legos,® Transformers,® and other small toys
	Uses "just right" force when in physical contact with others	Uses inappropriate force when in contact with others, e.g., roughhousing or playing games such as "Ring Around the Rosy" or "The Farmer in the Dell," often pushing, shoving, squeezing, yanking, bumping, crashing, and "dive-bombing" into others
Visual	Recognizes own name in print	Cannot recognize own name in print
	Can tell the difference between similar pictures and symbols	Confuses likenesses and differences in pictures (apple or heart), symbols (△ or ♥)
	Concentrates on details in faces, puzzles, pictures, and storybooks	Has difficulty focusing on details in faces, puzzles, and pictures, and in "same and different" and "What's Wrong with this Picture?" activities
	Reads people's facial expressions and gestures	Misses important visual cues in social interactions, such as facial expressions and gestures
	Mimics other children in follow-the-leader games	Has difficulty mimicking other children in follow-the-leader games, such as "Simon Says"
	Scans a crowded page and locates a figure from the busy background	Has difficulty scanning a detailed book page to locate Waldo® in *Where's Waldo?*
	Selects jigsaw puzzle pieces that have a good chance of fitting, builds block towers, and chooses appropriate materials to design a recognizable face on a paper plate	Has difficulty with visual-spatial tasks, i.e., judging where things are in space and how things fit together, such as selecting jigsaw pieces to fit into a puzzle, building block towers, or designing a face on a paper plate with buttons, paper scraps, and other materials

Category 2: Sensory Discrimination (cont'd.)

Sense	Typical Child ("Aha!")	Sensory Jumbler ("Huh?")
Visual (cont'd.)	Accurately judges where objects are in space and can build a tower of 5-10 blocks, avoid bumping into furniture, catch or kick a ball, and move in the same direction with a group of children	Has difficulty gauging where objects and people are in space, such as where to set blocks to make a tower, how close she is to bumping into a table, how fast a ball is coming toward her, what direction the other kids are moving in a parade
	Goes from one place to another without getting lost ("wayfinding")	Has difficulty "wayfinding" (finding the way from playground to classroom, or from classroom to bathroom)
Auditory (Hearing)	Understands subtle differences in word sounds, such as cap vs. cat (by 4 or 5)	Has difficulty recognizing the difference between sounds, especially consonants at ends of words, e.g., cap/cat, back/bag, side/sign
	Enjoys hearing, repeating, and making up rhymes (by 4 or 5)	Has difficulty repeating rhymes and making up rhymes (by 4 or 5)
	Sings more or less in tune	Sings way out of tune
	Understands difference between "put the book on the block" and "put the block on the book"	Becomes easily confused by verbal instructions, such as "put the book on the block," perhaps putting the block on the book instead
	Follows verbal directions without looking to others for cues	When trying to follow verbal directions, looks to others for visual cues
	Identifies classmates' and teachers' voices	Has trouble identifying voices unless he can see who is speaking
	Can focus on teacher's voice despite background chatter	Has poor ability to pick out a sound from a noisy background and cannot pay attention to one voice or sound without being distracted by other sounds
	Has good sense of rhythm and timing when clapping, marching, etc.	Has poor sense of timing and rhythm and frequently is off the beat when clapping, marching, playing rhythm band instruments, singing, or jumping rope
Olfactory (Smell)	Notices unusual aromas	Does not notice unusual aromas, such as melted crayons
	Can distinguish smells, such as lemon, vinegar, chocolate, cinnamon, soap	Cannot distinguish distinct smells, such as lemon, vinegar, chocolate, cinnamon, or soap
Gustatory (Taste)	Notices unusual flavors	Does not notice unusual flavors, such as cloves in pumpkin pie or anise in Christmas cookies
	Can distinguish tastes, and knows when snacks are spicy, salty, sour or sweet	Cannot distinguish tastes (chocolate vs. vanilla) or tell when snacks are spicy, salty, sour, or sweet

Category 3: Sensory-Based Motor Skills
Good Postural Responses vs. Postural Disorder (difficulty stabilizing the body while moving or resting in response to the sensory demands of the environment or task)

Components of normal movement patterns	Typical Child ("I'm ready!" on Individual Child's Checklist)	Sensory Slumper ("Don't want to!" on Individual Child's Checklist)
Muscle tone	Has firm muscle tone, "at the ready" to react and move	Has low muscle tone and a "loose and floppy" body
	Has the strength and endurance to keep up with peers	Lacks strength and endurance and is often unable to keep up with peers in activities such as "Clap, Clap, Clap Your Hands"
Motor control	Bends and straightens joints smoothly	Has difficulty bending and straightening joints for "up-down" activity songs and pretending to be falling raindrops
Cocontraction	Uses muscles around joint to maintain stability and has good grasp on objects	Has a loose grasp on objects such as doorknobs, faucets, toys, blocks, paintbrushes, lunch boxes, and Tug-of-War ropes

Category 3: Sensory-Based Motor Skills—Postural Responses (cont'd.)

Components of normal movement patterns		Typical Child ("I'm ready!" on Individual Child's Checklist)	Sensory Slumper ("Don't want to!" on Individual Child's Checklist)
Balance		Keeps balance while moving from one ground surface to another	Has difficulty maintaining balance while moving to different ground surfaces, such as stepping out of car onto sidewalk, or from clatter bridge to sandbox
		Sits on floor with legs crossed or straight out	At circle time, sits on floor in "W" position, with legs bent, knees forward, and feet splayed out to the sides
		Sits on chair with legs in front, feet on floor	Sits on chair with legs wrapped around chair legs
		Maintains balance when standing and walking	Loses balance easily and frequently "trips on air"
		Easily changes positions and regains centered, upright posture	Loses balance when changing positions, such as bending to pick up dropped toy, playing musical games such as "Head and Shoulders, Knees and Toes," standing on one foot, hopping, or walking on beam
Stability		Can "hold on and stay put"	Has difficulty maintaining stable posture, e.g., falls over easily when pushed, cannot "hold on and stay put" on moving object like sled, scooter, swing, or see-saw
		Can use hand or foot for isolated movement without engaging body	"Fixes," i.e., tightens body parts, such as pressing elbow to ribs when drawing, because of difficulty in doing isolated movements without engaging body
Flexion		Uses muscles to bend joints, such as flexing hips to walk upstairs	Has difficulty flexing muscles against gravity, e.g., has a problem going up stairs, and, when lying on his back, cannot do a sit up
Weight bearing		Enjoys different kinds of movement, e.g., creeping and crawling	Has difficulty creeping like a cat on all fours, crawling like an alligator by pulling body forward with arms and legs, and pushing hands against the floor to raise the upper body in a Cobra movement
Weight shift		Rocks back and forth and side to side while standing or sitting	Has difficulty moving body back and forth or side to side across the midline, e.g., cannot rock forward and back while playing "Row, Row, Row Your Boat" or shift from one foot to another like a ding-dong bell in "Frère Jacques"
Rotation		Can move an arm or leg around central axis of body without twisting body as a whole	Has difficulty moving arms or legs around her central body axis; e.g., when looking around or stretching toward an object, turns body as a whole
Bilateral coordination		Uses both sides of body together	Has difficulty using both sides of the body together for jumping symmetrically, holding swing ropes and pumping, catching ball, beating tom-tom, clapping, popping bubbles, or using rolling pin
		Uses one hand to assist the other	Has difficulty using one hand to assist the other, e.g., holding cup while pouring juice, steadying paper while drawing, zipping jacket
		Uses one foot to assist the other	Has difficulty using one foot to assist the other, e.g., for going upstairs or for "dusting" sand off one foot with the other foot
		Has a hand preference (by age of 4) and uses it to reach out directly to retrieve object	Has not yet established a hand preference (by age of 4) and uses either hand to reach for block, pitcher, cup, tambourine or triangle
		With preferred hand, manipulates small object	Uses first one hand and then the other, clumsily, to manipulate counting bears, board game pieces, needle for lacing beads, crayons, scissors, etc.
Crossing the midline		Uses one eye, hand, or foot in the space of the other eye, hand, or foot	Has difficulty crossing the midline to paint a horizontal horizon from left to right with one hand at the easel, or to sweep arms across body to make the "wipers on the bus go swish, swish, swish"

Category 3: Sensory-Based Motor Disorder
Praxis vs. Dyspraxia (difficulty in thinking of an unfamiliar, multi-step action, doing the motor planning to sequence the steps, and carrying out the motor plan)

Components of Praxis	Typical Child ("I can do this.")	Sensory Fumbler ("I can't do that.")
Thinking	Conceptualizes an unfamiliar action involving several steps	Has difficulty conceiving of what she can do or would like to do, e.g.: • Getting into a fancy new dress-up in the Make-Believe Corner • Thinking of "another part of your body to shake, shake, shake" • Designing a person or house with construction paper shapes • Passing around birthday cupcakes • Getting into position on all fours to crawl through a tunnel • Thinking of different ways to use simple objects such as a string, hoop, scarf, or paper towel tube
Motor planning	Gets ready and organizes her body to carry out the multi-step plan she has thought up (or a plan she intends to follow)	Has difficulty sequencing the steps and organizing her body movements for carrying out the new and complex plan that she has conceptualized (or another person's plan that she intends to follow or imitate)
Execution (carrying out)	Carries out the new plan, or makes some progress	Is uncoordinated and clumsy in carrying out the multi-step motor plan
Gross-motor	Moves body through space smoothly, with good coordination	Has poor motor coordination, moving in a clumsy way, especially when trying to navigate around tables and easels in a classroom or across a busy playground
	Gets into and out of some clothing, such as jacket, footwear, etc.	Has difficulty with most dressing skills, such as getting into and out of sweater, jacket, socks and boots, and pulling pants down and up for toileting
	Succeeds most of the time with gross-motor activities	Is awkward doing gross-motor activities, such as walking, running, kicking a ball, climbing stairs or ladder, sliding, jumping, tiptoeing, marching, crawling, and rolling
	Mounts and rides new ride-on toys	Has difficulty mounting and riding tricycles, scooters, and Big Wheels,® especially for the first time
	Figures out how to orient body in obstacle courses	Has difficulty adapting body to go through obstacle courses without assistance
Fine-motor	Uses classroom tools	Has difficulty with manipulative tasks and classroom tools, e.g., using markers, crayons, pencils, scissors, hole punchers, tongs, glue bottles, brushes, lacing needles, hammers, and xylophone mallets
	Shows interest in squiggling and drawing and pretends to "write"	Has difficulty manipulating a crayon or marker to squiggle, draw, or pretend to "write"
	Manipulates small objects	Has difficulty manipulating small toys, counting rods, jigsaw puzzle pieces, and placing raisins on celery sticks to make "Ants on a Log"
	Succeeds at many dressing details	Has difficulty with dressing details requiring finger and hand dexterity, e.g., zipping and unzipping, buttoning, snapping, putting on mittens, and Velcroing® boots
	Succeeds at snack-time tasks	Has difficulty with snack-time tasks, e.g., pouring juice, opening cracker packages, spreading peanut butter, spooning applesauce, and picking up popcorn

Category 3: Sensory-Based Motor Disorder—Praxis vs. Dyspraxia

Motor Skill	Typical Child ("I can do this.")	Sensory Fumbler ("I can't do that.")
Fine-motor	Succeeds at self-help tasks in classroom that require fine-motor skills	Has difficulty with classroom self-help tasks, e.g., opening doors, drawers, boxes, watercolor trays, or "windows" in storybooks; sliding out jigsaw puzzles and replacing them in their racks; fitting jigsaw pieces into the puzzle; shaking dice or spinning Candyland dial; cleaning up a pile of Legos or counting rods, etc.
	Succeeds with playground tasks requiring fine-motor skills	Has difficulty with fine-motor playground tasks such as picking up acorns and pinecones, sorting seeds and pebbles into egg carton compartments, holding kite strings and jump ropes, plucking mulch off his sleeve, etc.
Eye-motor	Can use both eyes together as a team	Has difficulty using both eyes together to shift visual attention from one sight to another in the environment around her
	Uses both eyes together for smooth pursuit (tracking) of a moving object	Has difficulty with smooth pursuit (tracking) of moving objects, such as watching a car driving by, a bird in flight, another child swinging, or a ball or balloon coming toward him
	Focuses on people or objects in the space around him	Has difficulty focusing on objects and people in his personal space or in the classroom and on the playground
	Can shift gaze from side to side or from a faraway point to a nearby point without moving body	Has difficulty shifting gaze from side to side or from faraway point to nearby point, e.g., looking out the window at his peanut-butter-and-pinecone birdfeeder and then down to a paintbrush in his hand, without also moving his whole body along with his eyes
	Has good visual-motor skills for connecting what he sees (visual input) with how he moves and what he does (motor output)	Has difficulty connecting visual information with how he moves or what he does, e.g., seeing the swing across the playground and walking toward it, maneuvering around other children and classroom obstacles, cutting out a paper shape along the lines, arranging collage materials or lunch box items in his personal table space
Oral-motor skills and Speech	Eats and chews with mouth closed and not much messiness	Eats and chews with mouth open and excessive messiness; drools excessively
	Blows bubbles	Has difficulty blowing bubbles
	Sucks through a straw	Has difficulty sucking through a straw
	Pronounces speech sounds relatively clearly	Has difficulty producing and articulating speech sounds (phonemes) including: p, m, h, n, and w (by age 3) b, k, g, d, f, and y (by age 4)
	Speaks clearly enough to be understood by most	Has difficulty pronouncing words clearly enough to be understood by most strangers

This list includes basic information about selected therapies and professionals that may benefit a child with Sensory Processing Disorder. For more details, follow the links or see www.SPDnetwork.org.

Primary Therapies

Occupational therapy using a sensory integration framework (OT/SI)

Professional: Occupational Therapist

Occupational therapy is the use of purposeful activity to maximize the independence and maintenance of health of an individual who is limited by a physical injury or illness, cognitive impairment, a psychosocial dysfunction, a mental illness, a developmental or learning disability, or an adverse environmental condition. The practice encompasses evaluation, assessment, treatment, and consultation. For a child, purposeful activities include swinging, climbing, jumping, buttoning, and drawing. Such activities are the child's "occupation."

An occupational therapist is a health professional that has received a baccalaureate or M.A. after completing a course of study, plus internship experience, in biological, physical, medical, and behavioral sciences. (After January 1, 2007, all new occupational therapy candidates will require a post-baccalaureate degree.) Coursework includes neurology, anatomy, orthopedics, psychology, and psychiatry.

The occupational therapist may work with the child individually or in a group, at school, in a clinic, hospital, community mental health center, or home. The ideal occupational therapist is one who specializes in pediatrics and who has received additional, postgraduate training in sensory integration theory and treatment. The specific goals of occupational therapy using a sensory integration (OT/SI) framework are to improve the person's social participation, self-esteem, self-regulation, and sensory-motor abilities.

Under the guidance of a therapist, the child actively takes in movement and touch information in playful, meaningful, and natural ways that help his brain modulate these fundamental neural messages. The child responds favorably to SI treatment, because his nervous system is pliable and changeable. Therapy teaches the child to succeed—and he loves it!

Contact Information

To find an occupational therapist certified to diagnose and treat sensory processing problems, search (for free) in the National SPD Resource Directory at www.SPDnetwork.org for therapists near you. Or (for a small fee) go to Developmental Delay Resources, www.devdelay.org.

Physical therapy

Professional: Physical Therapist

Physical therapy is a health profession devoted to improving an individual's physical abilities. It involves activities that strengthen the child's muscular control and motor coordination, especially of his large muscles. Sometimes using physical agents such as massage, whirlpool baths, or ultrasound, physical therapists help the child get his muscles ready for voluntary movement. Some physical therapists receive additional training in sensory integration theory and treatment.

Contact Information

American Physical Therapy Association, www.apta.org.

Secondary Therapies

Auditory therapy, or auditory training

Professional: Audiologist, Speech-Language Pathologist, Occupational Therapist, or other qualified specialist

A method of sound stimulation designed to improve a person's listening and communicative skills, learning capabilities, motor coordination, body awareness, and self-esteem. Various methods employ the use of special headphones. Over several days, the child listens passively to music and voices filtered through the headphones and then participates in active voice work, such as repeating sounds, reading aloud, and conversing. Therapy helps the ear to attend to and discriminate among sounds, the vestibular system to integrate sensory messages of balance and posture, and the person to become more focused, centered, and organized. The Therapeutic Listening Program, designed by Sheila Frick, OTR/L, is an excellent home program that is supervised by a therapist while the child is receiving services.

Contact Information

See: www.tomatis.net or www.VitalLinks.net/auditory.html

Brain Gym®

Professional: Licensed Brain Gym Practitioner

The Brain Gym® system is a set of 26 specific movements developed by Paul Dennison, PhD, based on research in Educational Kinesiology. Educational Kinesiology studies education, child development, and physical movement of the human body as it relates to learning and expression skills. The system readies the body to learn by integrating visual, auditory, and kinesthetic functioning. It stimulates the nervous system equally in all brain parts, minimizes one-sided brain reactions, and strengthens neural pathways between the two hemispheres. The activities effect rapid and often dramatic improvements in concentration, memory, reading, writing, organizing, listening, physical coordination, and more.

Contact Information

ww.braingym.org

Chiropractic

Professional: Chiropractor

Chiropractic is the philosophy, art, and science of detecting and correcting subluxation in the human body. Subluxation is a partial dislocation or abnormal movement of a bone in a joint. Chiropractic helps children with SPD by specifically addressing the structure and function of the nerves, muscles, and joints controlling posture and movement that influence our ability to interact with our environment.

Contact Information

www.icpa4kids.com or www.chiroweb.com/find/children.html

CranioSacral therapy (CST)

Professional: Occupational Therapist, Physical Therapist, Chiropractor, Osteopath, Massage Therapist, or other Registered Craniosacral Practitioner (RCST)

CST is a gentle method of evaluating and enhancing the function of the craniosacral system (the membranes and cerebrospinal fluid that protect the brain and spinal cord). CST involves light-touch manipulation of the bones in the skull, sacrum, and coccyx to correct an imbalance that can adversely affect the development of the brain and spinal cord and can result in sensory, motor, and neurological dysfunction. Developed by Dr. John Upledger, CST is used by a variety of healthcare professionals.

Contact Information

The Upledger Institute, www.upledger.com, 800-233-5880, or www.craniosacraltherapy.org

Hippotherapy (therapy with a horse)

Professional: Certified Instructor

Hippotherapy means "treatment with the help of the horse." Occupational, physical and speech therapists use the horse as a modality to improve the posture, movement, neuromotor function, and sensory processing of people with disabilities. The movement of the horse, with traditional therapy intervention, influences muscle tone, encourages muscle action, and improves vestibular reactions, sensorimotor integration, and midline postural control.

Contact Information

North American Riding for the Handicapped Association, www.narha.org, 800-369-RIDE; or Center for Equine Facilitated Therapy, www.nceft.com

Nutritional therapy, Dietary intervention

Professional: Nutritionist

Good nutrition is essential for development, efficient maintenance and functioning, optimum activity level, and resistance to infection and disease. A nutritionist can help a person with nutritional deficiencies achieve balance in carbohydrates, fats, protein, vitamins, minerals, and water.

Contact Information

Autism Network for Dietary Intervention, www.AutismNDI.com

Perceptual motor therapy

Professional: Perceptual Motor Therapist

Perceptual motor therapy provides integrated movement experiences that remediate gross motor, fine motor, and visual perception problems. Activities, including sensory input techniques, stimulate left- and right-brain communication to help the child interpret incoming information to the nervous system. Goals are to improve visual motor perception, develop more mature patterns of response to specific stimuli, improve motor skills and balance, and stimulate alternate routes to memory and sequencing for those children who do not respond to the methods taught in the conventional classroom.

Contact Information

GMS Institute–SI Division (Virginia), www.gmskids.org, (703) 369-7800; or Kids Moving Co. (Maryland), www.kidsmovingco.com, (301) 656-1543.

Psychotherapy

Professional: Psychotherapist, Clinical Psychologist, Licensed Clinical Social Worker, Psychiatrist

Psychotherapy is sometimes appropriate, particularly if the child has behavior or self-image problems or is depressed. (Psychotherapy deals with the effects of SPD, but not the underlying causes.) Psychotherapies include behavioral therapy, to help the child deal with problematical symptoms and behaviors; family therapy, to help the child, parents and siblings become a healthier unit; and play therapy, to promote the child's social-emotional development.

Contact Information

www.floortime.org

Speech and language

Professional: Speech-Language Pathologist (SLP)

Speech-language therapy includes activities designed to meet specific goals for the child. The child may need help with speech skills, such as pronouncing "L," "K," or "Sh" sounds; monitoring the pitch of his voice; and strengthening oral-motor control in the muscles of his mouth. He may also benefit from activities designed to expand his language skills, such as retelling stories, conversing, and playing games to develop memory and vocabulary. As many children with SPD are picky eaters, therapy with a speech pathologist trained in oral-motor and feeding issues may be very helpful. Optimal benefits occur when a child receives coordinated treatment from both a speech-language pathologist and an occupational therapist trained in oral-motor therapy.

Contact Information

American Speech-Language-Hearing Association (ASHA), www.asha.org or 1-800-638-TALK.

Vision Therapy, or Vision Training (VT)

Professional: Developmental (or Behavioral) Optometrist

Vision therapy, or optometric visual training, helps the person improve visual skills and can also prevent learning-related visual problems. Along with lenses or prisms, VT helps the child integrate visual information with input from other senses, such as hearing, touching, and moving. A developmental optometrist provides sensory-motor and educational activities that strengthen eye-motor control, eye-hand coordination and depth perception, and help develop visual perception.

Contact Information

Contact www.optometrists.org; or Optometric Extension Program Foundation: www.oep.org, (949) 250-8070; or Parents Active for Vision Education: www.pavevision.org, 800-PAVE-988.

Auditory: Pertaining to the ability to receive and understand sounds.

Behavior: Whatever one does, through actions, feelings, perceptions, thoughts, words, or movements, in response to sensory stimulation.

Bilateral coordination: The ability to use both sides of the body together in a smooth, simultaneous, and coordinated manner.

Body awareness: The mental picture of one's own body parts, where they are, how they interrelate, and how they move.

Body position: The placement of one's head, limbs, and trunk. (**Proprioception** is the sense of body position.)

Cocontraction: The simultaneous coordination of flexor and extensor muscles around a joint to maintain stability. Flexor muscles work to bend a joint, so a person can grasp and pull. Extensor muscles work to straighten the neck, back, or limbs, so a person can stretch and reach.

Crossing the midline: Using an eye, hand, or foot in the space of the other eye, hand, or foot.

Discrimination: Distinguishing differences among and between stimuli.

Dyspraxia: Dysfunction in praxis, i.e., difficulty in conceiving of, planning, and carrying out a novel motor action or series of motor actions.

Early intervention: Treatment or therapy to prevent problems or to improve a young child's health and development, such as eyeglasses or ear tubes for medical problems, and occupational therapy or speech-language therapy for developmental problems.

Environment: The circumstances or conditions surrounding a person.

Evaluation: The use of assessment tools, such as tests and observations, to measure a person's developmental level and individual skills, or to identify a possible difficulty.

Eye-hand coordination: The efficient teamwork of the eyes and hands, necessary for activities such as playing with toys, dressing, and drawing.

Fine-motor: Referring to movement of the small muscles in the fingers, toes, eyes, and tongue.

Fixing: Pressing one's elbows into one's sides or one's knees together for more stability.

Flexion: Movement of the muscles around a joint to pull a body part toward its front or center; bending.

Force or Grading: The body's ability to judge the motion of the muscles and joints according to how much pressure is necessary to exert in relation to objects in the environment.

Gross-motor: Referring to movement of large muscles in the arms, legs, and trunk.

Gustatory sense: The sense of perceiving flavor; taste.

Hand preference: Right- or left-handedness, which becomes established gradually (by the age of 4) as the young brain matures.

Inner drive: Every person's self-motivation to participate actively in experiences that promote sensory processing.

Interoceptive: Pertaining to the sense involving both the conscious awareness and the unconscious regulation of bodily processes of internal organs.

Language: The organized use of words and phrases to interpret what one hears or reads and to communicate one's thoughts and feelings.

Meltdown: The process, usually caused by excessive sensory stimulation, of becoming "undone" or "unglued," accompanied by screaming, writhing, and deep sobbing.

Midline: A median line dividing the two halves of the body.

Modulation: The brain's ability to regulate and organize the degree, intensity, and nature of the person's response to sensory input in a graded and adaptive manner.

Motor control: The ability to regulate and monitor the motions of one's muscles for coordinated movement.

Motor coordination: The ability of several muscles or muscle groups to work together harmoniously to perform movements.

Motor planning: The ability to organize and sequence the steps of an unfamiliar and complex body movement in a coordinate manner; a part of praxis.

Muscle tone: The degree of tension normally present when one's muscles are relaxed, or in a resting state.

Occupational therapy (OT): The use of activity to maximize the independence and the maintenance of health of an individual who is limited by a physical injury or illness, cognitive impairment, psychosocial dysfunction, mental illness, developmental or learning disability, or adverse environmental condition. OT encompasses evaluation, assessment, treatment, and consultation.

Olfactory sense: The sense of perceiving odor; smell.

Oral-motor skills: Movements of muscles in the mouth, lips, tongue, and jaw, including sucking, biting, crunching, chewing, and licking.

OT/SI: Occupational therapy using a sensory integration framework.

Overresponsivity: Observable behavior involving a quick or intense response to sensory stimuli that others usually perceive as benign; characterized by exaggerated, negative, and emotional responses or withdrawal.

Perception: The meaning that the brain gives to sensory input.

Physical therapy: A health profession devoted to improving one's physical abilities through activities that strengthen muscular control and motor coordination, especially of the large muscles.

Postural disorder: Difficulties with stabilizing the body while moving or resting in different positions in response to the sensory demands of the environment or task.

Postural response: Assuming or maintaining a stable position and moving into and out of positions without losing one's balance.

Praxis: The ability to conceptualize, to plan and organize, and to carry out a sequence of unfamiliar actions; to do what one needs and wants to do in order to interact successfully with the physical environment. ("Motor planning" is often used as a synonym.)

Proprioception: The unconscious awareness of sensations, coming from receptors in one's muscles, joints, and tendons, that provides information about when and how muscles contract or stretch; when and how joints bend, extend, or are pulled; and where each part of the body is and how it is moving. Proprioception is the "muscle sense" or the "body position sense."

Protective extension: Thrusting out one's arms or a leg to protect oneself when falling.

Rotation: The ability to move the body asymmetrically around one's central axis.

Scan: In this context, a quick examination.

Screening: A procedure for the early identification of health or developmental problems.

Self-help skills: Competence in taking care of one's personal needs, such as dressing, eating, and toileting.

Self-regulation: The ability to control one's activity level and state of alertness, as well as one's emotional, mental, or physical responses to sensations; self-organization.

Sequencing: Putting movements, sounds, sights, objects, thoughts, letters, and numbers in consecutive order, according to time and space.

Sensory-based motor disorder: A problem with movement, such as **Postural Disorder** or **Dyspraxia**, resulting from inefficient sensory processing.

Sensory diet: The multisensory experiences that one normally seeks on a daily basis to satisfy one's sensory appetite; a planned and scheduled activity program that an occupational therapist develops to help a person become more self-regulated.

Sensory integration (SI): The part of sensory processing whereby sensations from one or more sensory systems connect in the brain. ("**SI dysfunction**" is another term for **SPD**.)

Sensory integration treatment: A technique of occupational therapy, which provides playful, meaningful activities that enhance an individual's sensory intake and lead to more adaptive functioning in daily life. The emphasis is on improving sensory-motor processing rather than on skill training.

Sensory-motor: Pertaining to the brain-behavior process of taking in sensory messages and giving a physical response.

Sensory modulation disorder: The inability to regulate the degree, intensity, and nature of responses to sensory input.

Sensory Processing Disorder (SPD): Difficulty in the way the brain takes in, organizes, and uses sensory information, causing a person to have problems interacting effectively in the everyday environment. Sensory stimulation may cause difficulty in one's movement, emotions, attention, relationships, or adaptive responses.

Sensory seeking: The constant quest for excessive sensory stimulation.

Smooth pursuit: The ability to use both eyes together as a team to follow a moving object in its track.

Social skills: Effective interaction and communication with others, necessary for developing and keeping friendships.

Speech: The physical actions of communicating a verbal message.

Stability: The ability to maintain equilibrium or resume one's original, upright position after displacement, such as being jostled in line or moved on the playground swing.

Stimulus (pl., **stimuli**): Something that activates a sensory receptor (a special cell located in the body that receives specific sensory messages), and produces a response.

Tactile sense: The sensory system that receives sensations of pressure, vibration, movement, temperature, and pain, primarily through receptors in the skin and hair.

Touch pressure: The tactile stimulus that causes receptors in the skin to respond. A bear hug provides deep touch pressure; a kiss provides light touch pressure.

Underresponsivity: Undersensitivity to sensory stimuli, characterized by a tendency either to crave intense sensations or to withdraw and be difficult to engage; a subtype of **sensory modulation disorder**.

Unilateral coordination: Smooth, independent use of one side of the body, necessary for drawing and handling tools.

Vestibular sense: The sensory system that responds to changes in head position, to body movement, and to the pull of gravity. It coordinates movements of the eyes, head, and body, affecting balance, muscle tone, visual-spatial perception, auditory-language perception, and emotional security.

Vision: The process of identifying sights, understanding what the eyes see, and preparing for a response.

Visual-motor skills: Ability to connect what one sees with how one moves (walking over to the swing) or what one does (cutting on the lines).

Wayfinding: Going from one place to another without getting lost, or finding one's way in a new place.

Weight shift: Asymmetrical movement of one's body mass across the midline.

Selected Bibliography

Ayres, A. Jean (2005). *Sensory Integration and the Child: Understanding Hidden Sensory Challenges.* Los Angeles: Western Psychological Services.

Bundy, Anita C., Shelly J. Lane, & Elizabeth A. Murray (2002). *Sensory Integration: Theory and Practice,* 2nd Ed. Philadelphia: F.A. Davis.

Henry, Diana (1998). *Tool Chest for Teachers, Parents & Students: A Handbook to Facilitate Self-Regulation.* Accompanies two videotapes: *Tools for Students: OT Activities for Classroom & Home,* and *Tools for Teachers: an Overview of School Based Occupational Therapy.* Henry Occupational Therapy Services, www.ateachabout.com

———, Maureen Kane-Wineland, & Susan Swindeman (in press). *Tools for Tots: Sensory Strategies for Toddlers, Their Caregivers, Teachers and Therapists.* Henry Occupational Therapy Services, www.ateachabout.com

Hurley, Donna S. (2001). *Sensory Motor Activities for the Young Child.* Bisbee, AZ: Imaginart International.

Kashman, Nancy, & Janet Mora (2005). *The Sensory Connection: Sensory and Communication Strategies that WORK!* Las Vegas: Sensory Resources.

Koomar, Jane, Carol Kranowitz, Stacey Szklut, Lynn Balzer-Martin, Elizabeth Haber, Deanna Iris Sava (2001). Manual: *Answers to Questions Teachers Ask About Sensory Integration: Forms, Checklists, and Practical Tools for Teachers and Parents.* Las Vegas: Sensory Resources.

———, Barbara Friedman, & Elizabeth Woolf, illus. (1992). *The Hidden Senses: Your Muscle Sense, and The Hidden Senses: Your Balance Sense.* Rockville, MD: AOTA.

Kranowitz, C. S. (2005). *The Out-of-Sync Child: Recognizing and Coping with Sensory Processing Disorder,* rev. ed. New York: Perigee.

———. (2004). *The Goodenoughs Get in Sync: A Story for Kids about Sensory Processing Disorder.* Las Vegas: Sensory Resources.

———. (2003). *The Out-of-Sync Child Has Fun: Activities for Kids with Sensory Integration Dysfunction.* New York: Perigee.

———. (1995). *101 Activities for Kids in Tight Spaces.* New York: St. Martin's.

———. (2002). Videotape: *Getting Kids in Sync: Sensory-Motor Activities to Help Children Develop Body Awareness and Integrate Their Senses.* Las Vegas: Sensory Resources.

———. (2001). Videotape: *The Out-of-Sync Child.* Las Vegas, Sensory Resources.

———, & Stacey Szklut (1999). CD: *Teachers Ask About Sensory Integration.* Las Vegas: Sensory Resources.

Miller, Lucy Jane, with Doris Fuller (in process). *Sensational Kids: Hope and Help for Children with Sensory Processing Disorder.* New York: Putnam.

Miller, Lucy Jane, Sharon Cermak, Shelly Lane, Marie Anzalone, & Jane Koomar (2004). "Position statement on terminology related to sensory integration dysfunction." *S.I. Focus* magazine, Summer 2004. www.SIfocus.com

Murray-Slutsky, Carolyn, & Betty A. Paris (2005). *Is It Sensory or Is It Behavior? Behavior Problem Identification, Assessment, and Intervention.* San Antonio: PsychCorp.

Roley, Susanne Smith, Erna Imperatore Blanche, & Roseann C. Schaaf (2001). *Understanding the Nature of Sensory Integration with Diverse Populations.* Therapy Skill Builders.

Smith, Karen A., & Karen R. Gouze (2004). *The Sensory-Sensitive Child: Practical Solutions for Out-of-Bounds Behavior.* New York: Harper Collins.

Williams, Mary Sue, & Sherry Shellenberger (1992). *An Introduction to "How Does Your Engine Run?" The Alert Program for Self-Regulation.* Albuquerque: TherapyWorks.

Yack, Ellen, Shirley Sutton, & Paula Aquilla (2002). *Building Bridges through Sensory Integration,* 2nd ed. Las Vegas: Sensory Resources.

Many of these titles are available from Sensory Resources at www.SensoryResources.com or 888-357-5867.